Knock, Knock, "Who's Traveling?"

Dorinda Henderson

The history of customer service: "American businessman William Boyce [was] lost in a London fog and late for a business appointment in 1909. Out of the fog came a boy in uniform who offered to guide Boyce to his appointment, and did — and then refused a tip because, as he explained, he was a Scout, and Scouts did not take payment for good deeds. The legend is that Boyce later met with the founder of Scouting in Britain, Lord Baden-Powell, and then carried Scouting to the United States, incorporating the Boy Scouts of America on February 8, 1910." ("Quirks of History: Customer Service *Circa* 1909," *Millard Fillmore's Bathtub*, https://timpanogos.wordpress.com/2006/11/24/quirks-of-history-customer-service-circa-1909/). This was a paraphrase of what was considered as customer service in the 1900's and from someone in uniform that happened to a boy scout and trained to help someone in need of help and assistance. Well this is still called customer service in 2000's and it can be done in person or by phone. This book illustrates customer service by phone and given at its highest form of professionalism and consideration to people with similar situations as the man in 1909 that was lost in a London fog, but it's current situations are happening in various airports in the country.

Contents

Introduction..1

Day One 3

Day Two..13

Day Three 25

Day Four..36

Day Five..41

Day Six 47

Day Seven 57

Day Eight..67

Day Nine 71

Day Ten 74

Day Eleven..80

Day Twelve..83

Day Thirteen..86

Day Fourteen 89

Day Fifteen..93

Day Sixteen..97

Day Seventeen..100

Day Eighteen 103

Day Nineteen..107

Day Twenty..112

Day Twenty-One..117

Day Twenty-Two..128

Day Twenty-Three..146

Introduction

It happened some years ago. I was employed with an agency that handles large volumes of people in transportation and communication, known as customer service, and this particular service was performed over the phone. The position I held was of great importance to me, because I helped so many people from all walks of life. In the beginning this position was very exciting, challenging, and rewarding, because I knew that so many people depended on me giving them such vital information for traveling in and out of different parts of the world. The *who*s, *what*s, *where*s, and *why*s were so intriguing to me, and also made me say, "Wow, people don't really have a clue as to how this traveling business works."

The journey I'm about to take you on will be into the mindsets of thousands of people, their fears, doubts, confusion, worries, anger, happiness, sadness, and grievances, but mainly how misinformed they were. Some of these mindsets might shock you, some might make you say *awww*, some might leave you speechless, and some might make you say *hmm*. I hope you just enjoy reading and take some of the lessons and thoughts I've shared with you and enjoy your trip! And I truly hope I don't offend anyone by *race*, or *culture*, because that wasn't my intention when writing this book and for those *who* think I was offensive I apologize, cause those weren't real time answers! *JUST A THOUGHT*

Day One:

PHONE RINGS:

GREETING:
Hello, this is Airport Information, my name is _____; how may I help you?

CALLER QUESTION:
How much is parking at the airport? And where is it located?

RESPONSE:
Airport parking costs $2.00 a day and is located at the beginning of the airport. There are signs directing you into the parking lot, and there is a free shuttle bus taking you to and from the terminals. In addition to that there is parking right across from each terminal, which is called short-term parking. The cost for that is $4.00 per day, and that's in walking distance to the terminals. In either parking you can stay up to 30 days, but you have to let the parking attendant know this, so you won't be towed. The distance between the long-term parking lots and the terminals are about 2 ½ miles; that's why shuttle buses are provided.

CALLER QUESTION:
Thank you so much for the information, and you've answered all of my questions!
(Hold on, you're not getting away with thinking the rest of the upcoming questions are going to be as easy as that one was.) NOT!!! JUST A THOUGHT!!!

CALLER QUESTION:
I'm looking for my husband on a flight from California; what time will he land at your airport?

RESPONSE:
Now think about this two-part question: First, how would someone else have that information! Aren't you his wife? And why don't you have this information about your husband's flight status? Second, just to inform you, California is a state, not a city where flights come. I need more to help me help you, like what city in California your husband is flying from. And it would also help if you knew what airport he is coming into; you sound uncertain with that information as well. Are you sure this is your husband? It just seems you don't have any information right! JUST A THOUGHT!!!

(Just to mention this a bit early, people have this fallacious idea that airports are like homes, apartment buildings, offices, or any other structures that have physical addresses. The airport is a location where airlines take off and land. I've never heard of homes and apartment buildings landing and taking off flying anywhere. Please stop thinking and listen to yourself!) JUST A THOUGHT!!!

CALLER QUESTION:
Is the airport closed?

RESPONSE:
Why would the airport be closed?

CALLER QUESTION:
Oh, I heard on the radio that the airport was closed and I'm calling to check.

RESPONSE:
You do know when I answered the phone I said "Airport," so therefore the airport is open and fully functioning. My suggestion to you is turn your radio to an Earth station that speaks English and leave those alien stations alone! JUST A THOUGHT!!!

CALLER QUESTION:
I'm looking for my father on flight #730 from New Zealand, coming into Terminal X at 10 a.m. It's now 10 p.m. and I haven't heard from him. I tried calling the airline but no one's answering the phone.

RESPONSE:
If that flight was estimated to land at 10 a.m., why are you just now calling at 10 p.m. concerned about this flight? The reasonable time to call to check on a flight is at least 45 minutes after the flight has landed. If you're lucky and some airline personnel are still in the terminal where your father landed, and you get them on the phone, the concern for your father will seem very limited. It's 12 hours later, really! Sorry to say you have to wait until you hear from him and that's it. (It's 10 p.m.; do you know where your father is?) JUST A THOUGHT!!!

CALLER QUESTION:
Do you speak Spanish?

RESPONSE:
No, but you're speaking English! How can I help you? What airline information do you need? (Two basic questions.) Why the assumption that everyone in the USA has to speak or know Spanish. I'm not trying hold conversation with on back in our country and how is the family or talk bad around someone who you think doesn't understand or speak Spanish. I just want the facts as to why you are calling the airport. What I suggest is that you get some Rosetta Stone lessons and call me back when you learn how to ask for flight information! JUST A THOUGHT!!!

CALLER QUESTION:
I want a passenger paged, it's urgent!

RESPONSE:
The airport doesn't page passengers; there are too many terminals for that.

CALLER QUESTION:
The flight leaves at 9 a.m., I need them paged now!

RESPONSE:
It's 8:59 a.m.; why didn't you have that person paged earlier? Let me give you some insight to your situation: The airline does the paging for their passengers in their terminal, and the passenger may or may not hear the page. And that's only if the airlines hear the phone to answer; they are handling checking in passengers and really don't have the time to take a page. FYI, airlines board passengers 45 minutes before the flight, not one minute before, therefore the page may never be heard. And think about the times we are in now—it's called a cell phone, and they even have smartphones, which means you can text a person. Go back to the future! JUST A THOUGHT!!!

CALLER QUESTION:
I'm stuck on the highway, and I have a 1:45 p.m. flight to catch. It's 1:30 p.m.; can I make it? I need to call the airline and tell them I'm stuck on the highway!

RESPONSE:
Seriously, you're joking, right? That flight has pulled away from the gate and is probably about to taxi down the runway. Look, it's a bird, no, it's your plane taking off. People, people, when making your reservation yourself or with an airline agent, you must know that on domestic flights it's 2 hours before and on international flights 3 hours before. That means at the airport, not on the highway to the airport and then you got stuck in traffic or got a flat tire or had an accident. I don't care if you were hanging out all night and didn't get any sleep—you'd better follow those terms and conditions. You can sleep on the plane or sleep standing in the line to check in; someone will wake you up! JUST A THOUGHT!!!

CALLER QUESTION:
I gave my credit card to an agent over the phone for an airline ticket, but I can't remember her name or the airline I'm booked on. Can you help me?

RESPONSE:
Hmm! Surprising question; really not ready for this one but I'm going to try my best! Let me see, you called an airline to make a reservation and gave your credit card information to an agent, and you told her where you wanted to go and when you wanted to come back, and your credit card was approved. I'm going to give you a hint by saying, call your credit card company and find out from them the information you need to know about the airline, then call the airline and get your itinerary. And one

more word to the wise: stop letting your three-year-old make your reservation! JUST A THOUGHT!!!

CALLER QUESTION:
My cousin's uncle's father's daughter's mother's brother's son is coming in on a flight and I'm trying to track them down. Can you help me?

RESPONSE:
Time is of the essence, so therefore I don't need your family tree in order to help you! And if you don't have any more information to give other than that they are connecting to another flight from another country, no, I can't help you! What I can tell you is that out of all those people who are adults flying someone from one country to another, someone should have a cellphone to let you know what's happened in their travels—or else, by the time you finish running down the family tree, they may have already tried to contact you! JUST A THOUGHT!!!

CALLER QUESTION:
Did flight # 444 come in yet?

RESPONSE:
What's the name of the airline?

CALLER QUESTION:
Delta.

RESPONSE:
Hold one moment; yes, that flight has landed at the estimated time.

CALLER QUESTION:
Was the flight late?

RESPONSE:
Here we go! If I just told you that the flight landed, what difference does it make if it was late? I would think you would have concern if it didn't and feel grateful and relieved that it landed period. Maybe you were late, and the flight was on time, hmm! JUST A THOUGHT!!!

Before 9/11 the airports were a free, easy, and pleasurable experiences for most travelers with no qualms or fears. There were no harsh restrictions, no noticeable stares at any people working or traveling in the airports; it was a much friendlier atmosphere and workers being professional and helpful to hundreds of thousands of people using the airports on a daily basis. It's like the beginning when I mentioned helping people made me feel wanted and needed, by providing a good service for the flying public. The questions asked were examples of the callers before 9/11, and if you think those questions were somewhat redundant, hold on to your seats and experience the questions coming post-9/11. Since Homeland Security and its newly formed TSA agency arrived at the airports, it's become hectic. So, imagine the turmoil and confusion going on at the airports now. What was is no longer allowed in the airports will never go back to the way it used to be! The rules of the game have been changed, leaving very little room for compromising to protect the flying public.

It's an ongoing effort to secure the public and their rights while traveling through the airports. The philosophy goes, trust no one and suspect everyone! With the new effective rules enforced there are no exceptions that apply to the list of *do*s and *don't*s, the *can*s and *cannot*s, what's allowed on the planes. At first, it was very speculative as to what was permitted, and then TSA figured it out and ironed out some of the wrinkles. Now it's pretty much a known fact what cannot be bought on planes—i.e., matches, guns, water bottles, 3.8 ounces or more of fluids are prohibited. NO MORE, NO MORE, and there are host of other items that TSA has constructed on their web page www.tsa.gov. No longer can you hang out at the airports if you're picking up a passenger at the airport; you are not allowed, I repeat, not allowed, in the customs or immigrant areas or at the gate where the passengers depart for planes unless it's for an unaccompanied minor. No pets allowed unless traveling with a passenger, and there is no expectation to the rule. What a difference 9/11 made on the airport community—like overnight it seems like the norm.

CALLER QUESTION:
What can I bring on the plane?

RESPONSE:
This is an honest question it seems, right... No knifes, guns, 3.8 ounces of any fluids, razors, darts, chainsaws, etc. What can be bought on the plane are the following: food, baby food, wedding gowns, overhead bag, books, laptops, eyeglasses, DVDs, baby bag, women's purse, things of this nature.

CALLER QUESTION:
Can I bring bubble gum?

RESPONSE:
Hmm! Silence has come over me for a second, and I'm finding myself taking a deep breath before giving my answer. Have to be careful how I'm going to answer this question, so they get the full gist of what I'm saying. Okay, honestly, did you hear any of what I said you could bring on the plane? Bubble gum, really!

CALLER QUESTION:
Oh no, I was checking because I didn't know!

RESPONSE:
Let me clear up the dilemma in your mind. Pay very close attention to my words and what I'm going to say: bubble gum isn't a weapon or a threat to anyone but yourself, meaning you shouldn't chew it anymore—it might blow up in your mouth! JUST A THOUGHT!!!

Day Two:

WHAT'S WITH THE HOSTILE PASSENGERS calling and being rude and nasty to customer service; totally disrespectful to us. In my opinion the person asking for information they don't have on a family member or friend should be a bit humble to the person giving them the information they need. Be a bit more understanding of the fact that you're talking to another human being and we aren't a wall or a door that doesn't have or show feelings. We don't have a crystal ball on our desk to know the nature of your concerns, unless you calm down and speak to us with some decency and respect we deserve. We are here to help and serve customers that call seeking information about their friends and loved ones; this isn't a joke and we aren't here to misguide you in any way. We want to expedite this call, so you'll have all the information you need to move through the next process of the airport experience. There is a need to give some valuable tips, son, on how to do this without the frustrations, disrespect, cursing, and being nasty and obnoxious to customer service:

- Get to the point
- Know the name of the airline
- Have a destination or origin
- Listen carefully and don't interrupt; let the customer service agent finish before your questions
- Be calm

- Speak clearly and slowly
- Don't be judgmental to the agent trying to help you

CALLER QUESTION:
I want to know why I can't get information on my mother's flight? I've called six different numbers, and nobody can help me! I want to know what the F&%k is going on at that airport? I can't believe that you can't tell me anything about my mother coming on that F*%king flight, I'm going to write the mayor and the governor; this is some BULL S%*T! I want an answer now!

RESPONSE:
What airline is she coming on?

CALLER QUESTION:
I don't know, all I know is she landed at this airport. (This is when this caller makes a left turn and starts to get a bit out of control and quite ugly.) I want your supervisor; I don't want to talk to you anymore!

RESPONSE:
Have you called this number and spoken to anyone here about your situation?

CALLER QUESTION:
No.

RESPONSE:
Let's then start from the beginning with your problem; your frustration started when you couldn't reach anyone on the phone from the airline, correct?

CALLER QUESTION:
Correct.

RESPONSE:
After defusing this problem and getting some more information from this very honored person, I was able to direct them to the right airline and located this person's family member. The person became very humble and apologized for being so nasty and uncooperative at times during our conversation. Now the moral to this call is: you can catch more bees with honey than you can catch more flies with s%*t. JUST A THOUGHT!!!

CALLER QUESTION:
I want to bring an oversized garment bag on my flight; it has my wedding gown in it!

RESPONSE:
Did you phone the airline to see if they can accommodate your request? If not, you should have shipped the gown to your desti-nation via FedEx or UPS, because the airline won't allow you to bring oversize baggage as a carry-on.

CALLER QUESTION:
Yeah, but I don't have money to ship it, and why can't the airline let me put it overhead?

RESPONSE:
One good reason is it's airline policy not to have oversize baggage in the overhead compartment on the plane. And there is no

exception to the rules. And the real truth about your situation, really simple, if you can afford to get married in another country, then you should have made provisions to have your gown shipped safely to your hotel and put insurance on it. I mean, if you got money for that getting married on an island. Boom, problem solved! JUST A THOUGHT!!!

CALLER QUESTION:
My friend told me I needed a passport to go to Florida, and I called the airport to find out.

RESPONSE:
No, you don't need a passport to go to Florida! You're not going to Florence, Italy; your driver's license is sufficient to show the ticket counter and TSA. What did you learn in school? Remember the class your teacher was teaching about the 50 states in the United States? Perhaps you were absent for that class! JUST A THOUGHT!!!

CALLER QUESTION:
I'm traveling with three children ages three, two, and three months old. I want to know if they need IDs to travel?

RESPONSE:
The IDs that are required for children under the age of three are the parent's they would travel under, as long as the parent's ID is a city, state, or government ID. Your children don't drive, don't

have a job, aren't in the military, and your three-year-old may be in daycare and they don't give them photo ID to travel. So, let's make this easy for you in your travels, and bring their original birth certificates and your ID! JUST A THOUGHT!!!

CALLER QUESTION:
I want to fly to Vegas next week!

RESPONSE:
What's the airline you want to fly with?

CALLER QUESTION:
Give me XYZ or ABC airport.

RESPONSE:
As intelligent this person's question and answer may be, the answer this person gave me wasn't to the question I'd asked! I just smh and said these are the people who get up every day and think they are functioning in the right frame of mind. What is so scary is, this is the 21st century, and I'm talking to this person that honestly doesn't know that airports don't fly, airplanes do! REALLY...believe it!

CALLER QUESTION:
I didn't know what you meant when you asked what airline I want to fly with! I never flew before, so I don't know!

RESPONSE:

Okay, maybe if you stated that in the beginning of this conversation, you would have had what you needed to continue on like you had some sense. And acting like you were from another planet, or may you weren't acting and really didn't know! Here's the name of the airlines that go from XYZ or ABC airports that fly to Vegas. Remember, flying is fundamental, like reading, and you don't have to be astronaut to know this! JUST A THOUGHT!!!

CALLER QUESTION:

I need a ride to the airport; can someone come pick me up?

RESPONSE:

Who is that someone? Are you referring to ground transportation?

CALLER QUESTION:

Yes.

RESPONSE:

No, there is no ground transportation coming directly to your home to pick you up for the airport. What you need to do is get a Yellow Pages directory and look up private car services in your area, get you a limo service in your area, or call a friend to see if they can bring you to the airport, whatever comes first. Those are your choices, Ms. Daisy! JUST A THOUGHT!!!

CALLER QUESTION:
I lost my driver's license and I have a flight back to Chicago this afternoon!

RESPONSE:
This is a well-kept secret, but I'm going to let you in on it! Go to the nearest police station in the area and tell them you lost your driver's license and you have flight this afternoon. They will take a police report from you and give a slip of paper with a report number on it and the number of the police president. You bring that with you to the airport and show that to the ticket agent and the TSA agent.

CALLER QUESTION:
This happened months ago; I lost my wallet!

RESPONSE:
A word to the wise: don't tell them that. Do as though it just happened; if not, guess where your new residence will be? Not Chicago; instead it will be address unknown! JUST A THOUGHT!!!

CALLER QUESTION:
(This is a relay caller, which means an operator is on the other end typing what the person is saying and then the operator tells me. Most likely the person is deaf.) Do you have a currency exchange at the airport?

RESPONSE:
Yes.

CALLER QUESTION:
I just got off a flight and I want to exchange some currency; do you have currency exchange here?

RESPONSE:
Yes. What terminal did you arrive in? Because there are 15 passenger terminals at the airport. Terminals 1 through 15 have currency exchange.

CALLER QUESTION:
Caller repeats the same question!

RESPONSE:
I repeat the same answer to the question.

CALLER QUESTION:
Terminal 1 through 15.

RESPONSE:
Yes, finally a break in communication (this took every bit of 15 minutes just to get the terminal they wanted the number for)—wow, another satisfied customer. The reason it took so long is the operator had to wait for the person to type in the question, then the operator has to speak to me: wait for it! Then I answer the question and the operator has to type in my answer and the operator types back to the person to get their response.

CALLER QUESTION:
What time does the exchange close?

RESPONSE:

Okay, call this number, because I'll give you terminal information and location. They will give you the time they open and close. Look, I commend the operator who has been typing this; her fingers must be numb. The operator needed a relief operator like in baseball to come and take over for her pitch, and at that point the operator told me to hold on. Then it started to sound like Abbott and Costello Who's on 1st I don't What's on 2nd no That's on 3rd! JUST A THOUGHT!!!

CALLER QUESTION:

My mother left her asthma machine in the terminal; how can she get it back?

RESPONSE:

Really, asthma has to bring oxygen (air) to lungs in a matter of minutes. That's like saying, Oh, I left my lungs in the terminal. There are certain things you just don't play with, and that's one! That's like a fish out of water for some time. Watch what happens to that fish: ultimately it dies, so it seems like you have a backup pair of lungs! I'm surprised that didn't trigger an asthma attack just knowing your lifeline is nowhere near you. Take a deep breath, 'cause air is a terrible thing to waste! JUST A THOUGHT!!!

CALLER QUESTION:
I have a personal question; you may think it's weird (people in background laughing). The person asked if they could bring a dildo on the plane with them.

RESPONSE:
Nothing is weird at this point! Let me see if that's on the TSA list that I have; nope, so apparently that would be allowed on the plane. However, you may have to remove the batteries, and now that I think about it, it really depends on how it's going to be used; we don't want it blowing up inside someone that went to the bathroom and used it. Some people are into their feelings and get that sexual feeling and need sexual healing. Besides, it may be mistaken as a weapon of mass destruction for some! Really! JUST A THOUGHT!!!

CALLER QUESTION:
I'm at XYZ airport.

RESPONSE:
Okay, if you're at the airport why are you calling the airport?

CALLER QUESTION:
I need to ask some questions about my flight!

RESPONSE:
Okay, you do know you're at the airport and you have access to the airline ticket agent at the counter? If you're on time for your flight, the ticket agent and other airline personnel are there to

help passengers, so therefore that would be the time to ask your questions pertaining to your flight. What if I didn't answer and you were just holding on waiting for someone to answer who's not in the terminal? And you risk missing your flight, unless you already missed your flight and now you need to know your next alternative. What did I say earlier in this book: be on time for your flight 'because there are no exceptions to the rules: 2 hours domestic and 3 hours international. JUST A THOUGHT!!!

CALLER QUESTION:
Have a question?

RESPONSE:
Excuse me, I didn't hear what you were asking!

CALLER QUESTION:
What, you don't understand English?

RESPONSE:
I understand English quite well, it's my first and only language. It's that your accent is so heavy (from India) it's difficult to understand you! You have some nerve; you barely can formulate a sentence in English and you're questioning my ability to understand my language! Learn some English first before you start cursing and coming on the phone with your attitude, and then maybe I can listen to your accent! JUST A THOUGHT!!!

CALLER QUESTION:
When tipping the porter or baggage handler, do you receive a receipt?

RESPONSE:
No, you don't receive a receipt because it's a courtesy provided by the airline to their passengers; it's not like you're going to claim your tip with your tax preparer at the end of the year. You don't have to give them anything; they get a salary for doing their job. It's not a charity fund that can be used for tax purposes, and it's not like you're tipping hundreds of dollars! JUST A THOUGHT!!!

Day Three:

CALLER QUESTION:
I want to go to Costa Rica.

RESPONSE:
Where is Costa Rica?

CALLER QUESTION:
(Caller is laughing.) You don't know where Costa Rica is? It's in the Dominican Republic.

RESPONSE:
Okay, I made a mistake about knowing about where Costa Rica is but hold on now that I have the information to look up what flight goes here.

CALLER QUESTION:
I mean, why wouldn't you know this?

RESPONSE:
One reason is I don't frequent Costa Rica, so I wouldn't know off the top of my head what flights go there!

CALLER QUESTION:
Who else can I talk to that may know?

RESPONSE:
No one else but me; hold on while I find the airline or airlines that go. Hello, the following airlines go to Costa Rica: American and Lacsa.

CALLER QUESTION:
(Caller repeats) American and Lacsa!

RESPONSE:
Yes, that's what I said twice to answer your question, and now you sound like I'm not giving the right airlines. What's funny about your response is you don't know what airlines go to Costa Rica, for someone who comes from that country and flies there often and is a Dominican should know. Who's got the last laugh now! I want to speak to someone else who knows what airlines fly in and out of Costa Rica; do more homework before you go Debbie Downer on customer service that's trying to help you and maybe you can help as well. Instead of being a world-renowned traveler and having all the answers of all the airlines going all over the world, which by the way I do! JUST A THOUGHT!!!

CALLER QUESTION:
I lost my wallet at a bar and grill in terminal 12, do you have a number?

RESPONSE:
No, we don't receive bar and grill numbers in the terminals.

CALLER QUESTION:
So how can I get the number? Do you know the name of the place?

RESPONSE:
You mentioned it was a bar and grill, right? How is it that you don't know the name of a place in the airport that you just ate and had drinks at? Maybe it was the drinks, you had too many drinks and wiped out your memory! Advice: call your bank that your card comes from and get the name and number from them, you think! Hold your arms out and place one foot in front of the other! JUST A THOUGHT!!!

CALLER QUESTION:
I'm calling to find out where my bag is; it was lost at the airport.

RESPONSE:
Well, what airline were you traveling with?

CALLER QUESTION:
It was 10 or 12.

RESPONSE:
What is 10 or 12? You're giving me terminal numbers.

CALLER QUESTION:
So, what should I do?

RESPONSE:
Listen, miss, I can't guess what airline you traveled with in order for me to help you. You have to figure out the name of the airline you paid to fly with!

CALLER QUESTION:
Hold on while I get my airline ticket. Oh, here it is; it's B6.

RESPONSE:
That's JetBlue airways.

CALLER QUESTION:
Yeah, that's it!

RESPONSE:
Call the airline baggage number, which is ###-###-####, and then this is where the call went wrong! You don't remember what airline you flew with to find your baggage, smh once again! The baggage is a terrible thing to waste! JUST A THOUGHT!!!

CALLER QUESTION:
I want to return an airline ticket.

RESPONSE:
What do you mean you want to return your airline ticket? That's not going to happen. You change the flight and time you want to travel, which may be an open ticket for a year, but no returns on a purchased ticket. And this should be done at least 48 to 72 hours prior to you traveling; this way you may avoid a penalty. This isn't a department store where you may buy something, and you get it home and it doesn't fit, or you just don't like it, and you have your receipt and you take it back to either get a refund or store credit depending on the policy of the store. The airline business is selling tickets, selling tickets, selling tickets; nowhere

do you hear me say you will able to return your ticket. The thing the airlines will recognize is the word CANCELATION! And when you used that word you lose, or you choose to buy another ticket! JUST A THOUGHT!!!

CALLER QUESTION:
I'd like to go to Utah.

RESPONSE:
What airline? This is the universal question for mostly all these calls, which sets up the direction of the conversation and the outcome of the call.

CALLER QUESTION:
(Caller hangs up phone.)

RESPONSE:
It's 2017, stop, listen, think, then talk, or play back your words out on your family or friends. Talk in the mirror, record it, and play it back; just hear how you sound before saying anything of any intelligence. I know what I said and what I mean, but I don't know what you're trying to say or mean! JUST A THOUGHT!!!

IT'S SNOWING
Okay here comes the questions on the condition of the airport due to snow: is the airport open, why are they canceling flights, are the flights delayed, will the airline put us up in a hotel if we get stuck at the airport, can I cancel my flight because of the

snow, should I keep calling the airline to see if they are going to be on time, is the flight going to be late because of the snow, are they going to remove the snow so the airline can take off, when will the airport reopen the airport, will the airline be down, why do they have to de-ice the plane, will I get my money back if the airline doesn't fly in the snowstorm?

CALLER QUESTION:
My daughter was on one plane and they changed her to another flight. She said they were de-icing the plane. Do you think that's safe to de-ice the plane? And why didn't the airline cancel the flight?

RESPONSE:
Planes are being diverted all day and canceled due to the weather and de-icing the plane before it takes off is the safest thing the airline can do for its passengers—i.e., picture something weighing more than the object it's on, that's what water does to a plane; it becomes weight will affect the takeover of the aircraft . You would want that ice to melt, but it really doesn't matter what you want. It's safety first; and if you don't think so than you need to pull out your ice skates and start your own take off on the runway . JUST A THOUGHT!!!

CALLER QUESTION:
Oh, I'll try to speak English. I bought three tickets last year for a trip and I want to know how I get money back?

RESPONSE:
You don't get money back if you don't go on your flight!

CALLER QUESTION:
No, I want to know, do I pay a penalty or something.

RESPONSE:
No, you don't pay a penalty; you just lose your money or lost your money for those tickets!

CALLER QUESTION:
Oh, that's how it goes?

RESPONSE:
Yes. Let's look deep into this situation. You're talking about tickets you purchased last year and didn't go on the flight, and you didn't cancel to see if you could get open tickets, which means you could have still reserved those tickets to up to one year. As the saying goes, you're s*&t out of luck. Who does that? Or you just had an out-of-mind experience and just came back! JUST A THOUGHT!!!

CALLER QUESTION:
Anticipation!!! I'm calling about the weather tomorrow. Is the airport going to be closed today?

RESPONSE:
What!! No, why would the airport be closed today?

CALLER QUESTION:
I'm anticipating about tomorrow's storm!

RESPONSE:
Okay, let's get the days straight. Tomorrow is tomorrow and today is today, right? The airport reacts to weather when there is something to react to; if the weather gets to that severity then the airport communicates with the various airlines and everybody acts accordingly. Picture the airport or airline closing because of anticipation in the weather: it would be a financial disaster in the making. The airport-and-airline industry is a multi-trillion-dollar business and no rain, sleet, or snow is going to close it unless the storm is so horrific, like a total white where the pilots can't see the runways or taxiways, then yes, but not the day before an assumed snowstorm! JUST A THOUGHT!!!

CALLER QUESTION:
I'm going to Mexico tomorrow and I mailed for my passport; it hasn't arrived yet. Does the airport issue passports?

RESPONSE:
First of all, when did you plan your trip to Mexico? You should have had some time to send for your passport. It would seem logical to find out how long it would take from the time you applied for a passport and the time it's needed for travel, easy! Don't wait till 24 hours before and expect things to happen right now; that's why it's called planning, which includes timing! And no, the airport doesn't issue passports; you go to your local post office and do it! JUST A THOUGHT!!!

CALLER QUESTION:
How do I know what time my flight is leaving?

RESPONSE:
Did you make your reservations?

CALLER QUESTION:
No, actually this is for my aunt and she is leaving New York, going to Moscow, then changing flights for New Delhi. I'm looking on the ticket; can you help me find the time on the ticket?

RESPONSE:
This is fully loaded; it's time for psych 101 class. You have to read the ticket in its entirety. The airline name is usually printed on the ticket and you have read from left to right, and, guaranteed, that time and origin is on that ticket.

CALLER QUESTION:
I don't know! I will call my aunt and call back.

RESPONSE:
Why do you have to call your aunt to find out what flight she is taking? Why isn't your aunt calling herself; it's her flight. Better still, do this: don't call back; call Russia and ask for the airport in Moscow, then find out the information on your aunt's flight! JUST A THOUGHT!!!

CALLER QUESTION:
Hi, I'd like to know if my parents could come to the gate to say goodbye, because we are leaving the country for about three years.

RESPONSE:
Unfortunately, no; the only place you and your parents can say your goodbyes in is the terminal check-in area. What airline terminal are you flying from?

CALLER QUESTION:
Terminal 10.

RESPONSE:
What terminal are your parents using?

CALLER QUESTION:
Terminal 6. My flight is at 17:55 (which is 5:55); my parents' flight is at 21:40 (which is 9:40).

RESPONSE:
Okay, your parents can take the air train to Terminal 6 with you and spend the check-in time with until you go to your gate.

CALLER QUESTION:
I'm a bit confused about this; what if they change airlines and fly out of Terminal 8?

RESPONSE:
That's not going to work, because you're flying out of the international part of the terminal, and if they change flights they will be flying out of the domestic part of the terminal, so they won't be able to see you off, understand!

CALLER QUESTION:
There are no exceptions to the rule, so security will let my parents see me off?

RESPONSE:
Perhaps if you were handicapped and needed wheelchair assistance the airline might give them permission with a gate pass, and it might not be both of them.

CALLER QUESTION:
What if I call the airline and tell them my parents have mental problems about traveling by themselves, do you think that would work?

RESPONSE:
Really, that's not going to work either!

CALLER QUESTION:
Maybe if I call the airline.

RESPONSE:
What it seems like to me is that you are the one with the mental problem even saying some craziness like that to anyone. And why would you let your so-called mentally challenged parents fly to two different countries by themselves and then you want them to see you to your gate to say goodbye! Listen carefully to the dial tone 'in your ear; that's your goodbye! JUST A THOUGHT !!!

Day Four:

CALLER QUESTION:
Hello, I traveled last week, and I believe I left my book on the plane, is there any way you can find it? I'm in Chicago now!

RESPONSE:
WHAT!! (I'm taking the phone away from my ear to think about this one)... I'm back. Can you tell me what airline you flew with?

CALLER QUESTION:
I don't know, can't remember, how many flights go to Chicago?

RESPONSE:
That wasn't my question to you; I said what airline did you fly with?

CALLER QUESTION:
Funny; I travel all the time, I just can't remember. Can you look it up?

RESPONSE:
Are you serious? And no, I can't look up "I don't know" or "can't remember airline"! How scary is this—you paid for a flight, got on the flight, flew to and from on that flight, but you can't remember, and to add insult to injury you're looking for your

book you believe you left on the plane! Uhhhh, which way did they go, George, which way did they go, uhhh, I don't know! Tell you what, you should, after this conversation, and I mean immediately after this conversation, get rid of your frequent-flying privileges and give them to someone who knows the name of the airline they're about to board, and go buy another book but make sure it has a Lojack on it; this way you could track it! JUST A THOUGHT!!!

CALLER QUESTION:
I'm looking for Joe Cocomo.

RESPONSE:
Does he work at the airport or is he a passenger?

CALLER QUESTION:
I don't know where he works, I have a box for him and I'm just calling him to tell him.

RESPONSE:
Usually when a person says they don't know, they really don't, so why is this person pretending that he does? And why are you calling one of the biggest airports in the country to find out if this person works here without a name of a company, why? Then you act all kinds of surprised when the person on the other end of the phone can't help you! Let me call the airport and have the person answering the phone think for me! Make sense, not dollars, because you must not have money! JUST A THOUGHT!!!

CALLER QUESTION:
Is this airport information?

RESPONSE:
Yes, it is. (Mind you, I say this every time I answer the phone, every time.)

CALLER QUESTION:
Excuse me, I didn't hear you!

RESPONSE:
Funny you said, 'cause you repeated my hold introduction when answering the call!

CALLER QUESTION:
Anyway, is everything alright at the airport?

RESPONSE:
I believe so; why would you ask?

CALLER QUESTION:
I heard that there was a bomb threat at the fuel tanks!

RESPONSE:
Where did you get your information from?

CALLER QUESTION:
Oh, I just heard it and I'm checking because I'm a concerned citizen in a wheelchair!

RESPONSE:

Okay, I get the concern part...but what I don't get is, you're in wheelchair and not apparently scheduled for a flight and your concerns are what again ! My suggestion is to wheel yourself from in front of television and call when you're actually going to fly from the airport and request for wheelchair assistance the airline provides for their passengers needing that assistance! JUST A THOUGHT!!!

CALLER QUESTION:

Can I have an airline number?

RESPONSE:

Is this in reference to a flight, change in reservation, baggage, baggage storage, lost and found, pets, weight of luggage, the price of luggage?

CALLER QUESTION:

Can you give me the number you gave me before?

RESPONSE:

Oh, so you're a repeat caller. Was the number I gave for that airline a 1 800 000 0000? What happened when you called it?

CALLER QUESTION:

I called that number, and no one answered, and apparently you didn't understand that I wanted to speak with a person about my luggage!

RESPONSE:

Now, the truth will set you free! The lack of understanding or comprehension is on you. When we started this conversation and I stated the reference as to why you needed the airline number, you didn't say, I mentioned the number I gave you and you said you've tried and there was no answer. Well here's a news flash for you, that's the only number the airline gave to us to give to the public for any inquiries about their luggage! So, what I suggest you do is keep pressing that speed-dial button on your phone, go to the bathroom, take a shower, make you something to eat, perhaps get a nap in, and stop telling people what they don't understand what you need when you are calling airport information! JUST A THOUGHT!!!

Day Five:

CALLER QUESTION:
Could you please help me? I'm looking for a number about a part-time job at the airport, 'cause I need a job to help my grandfather!

RESPONSE:
We don't receive information on any part-time jobs at the airport. That's not the kind of information we provide; sorry!

CALLER QUESTION:
Oh, so do you have a number I can call?

RESPONSE:
Here I go again, going on a trip without my luggage, what was I thinking. First of all, you are calling looking for employment on a Sunday; secondly, you're not listening to what I just said. Let me break it down for you; when someone is talking to you, listen, then after they finish talking you give your response with an answer that relates to the conversation. And thirdly, who would hire you part time or anytime if you can't comprehend what is being asked of you to do the job? Even your probation officer knows you don't call looking for employment on a Sunday, but good try! JUST A THOUGHT!!!

CALLER QUESTION:
I'm calling to find out if my boss has a window seat on his flight?

RESPONSE:
The seating arrangements are made by the airline, or it can be done online when your reservations are made; it will give you a virtual look at the seats on the flight.

CALLER QUESTION:
The question is, a second party made the reservations and I don't know if they were made online!

RESPONSE:
Why don't you speak with the second party and find out if the reservations were made on online and take it from there, or else when the passenger goes to the ticket counter to check in they can find out then!

CALLER QUESTION:
Why can't I get this information beforehand?

RESPONSE:
Repeating myself again: why you can't is because I'm not the airline, so whoever made those reservations, I already gave my suggestion as to how to go about finding that information out! Is your boss afraid of height or does he suffer from vertigo? He or she won't see anything but clouds for the most part of their flight or tell them to pull the shutter down on the window. What I really see here is you messed up with your boss's itinerary and

you're trying to fix it! Lesson here: stop taking shortcuts and follow through with what your boss asked of you. Oh well, looks like you're not going to get that promotion!

CALLER QUESTION:
You are so rude while speaking to me!

RESPONSE:
Now, now sticks and stones will break my bones, but incompetency will never ever hurt me, believe that. And truthfully, you need to worry about what your boss will be saying to you after this screw-up, instead of worrying about how I sound. Again, when in doubt, that promotion may be out! JUST A THOUGHT!!!

Back from a well-deserved 10-day vacation and from the madness and mayhem, but the callers don't miss a beat...like reserved parking... RING RING, here comes my first call. Don't hold your breath, just keep reading, 'cause like wine, it's going to get better with time!

CALLER QUESTION:
I want to know, can I bring my infant's baby clothes with us on our flight, and her formula?

RESPONSE:
Yes, you can bring anything you need for that infant while in flight, and 50 pounds are allowed per luggage, plus you're allowed a baby bag...

CALLER QUESTION:
Someone told me to check with the airport first, and I have a lot of Pampers and formula and I don't want my things to get confiscated by the TSA.

RESPONSE:
If you and your infant are traveling more than 10 hours, I would think that you would want to change his or her clothes and the Pampers on the plane, especially if the baby gets hungry. That person who told you that should mind their business, because surely, they don't know what they are talking about. And that speaks for itself as far as being a mother to an infant, 'cause you couldn't be on a plane, train, or bus and your baby crapped on himself/herself and you don't try to go somewhere and change them. We would have a problem, and why would an airline take away the infant formula unless you're breastfeeding; how else would they eat? JUST A THOUGHT!!!

CALLER QUESTION:
My wife and kids are going to Ft. Lauderdale, Florida, and her driver's license has expired.

RESPONSE:
How long has her license been expired? You said four years ago.

CALLER QUESTION:
Can she still use it and bring her birth certificate?

RESPONSE:
Does she have a job ID?
CALLER QUESTIONS:
No, she doesn't work; she stays home and watches the kids!

RESPONSE:
Hold on. I transfer her to the airline and listen to the response of the airline, which was, yes, she can travel because she is going domesti-

cally, but this can only be a one-time occurrence. If in the future she wants to travel she will need to renew her non-driver's license.

CALLER QUESTION:
Hold on; my husband is talking to the airline representative at the airport; so, she can travel with her expired id! Maybe I'll make her go and renew it tomorrow!

RESPONSE:
Scratching my head now! If she is home all day and decided that she wanted to travel with her husband and then realizes her ID expired four years ago, guess what, she doesn't need to travel! Then her husband's mentality was that I made her go and renew! All I can say is, it must be nice to have a husband tell you when and where, do and not do pertaining to your ID. Wow, that couldn't be me; just have babies and not able to think on my own! Stepford wife! JUST A THOUGHT!!!,

CALLER QUESTION:
I need the number for customs, because I paid for puppies from Lagos, Nigeria, Africa!

RESPONSE:
What is the name of the cargo company the puppies are flying with?

CALLER QUESTION:
I don't know the cargo company. I don't have any more information to give you at this time!

RESPONSE:

It sounds like a scam going on, and you are another victim! What dogs are you getting from Africa that aren't wild and illegal in this country? You jumped a whole continent to buy some puppies and you don't have any information or know who the cargo company is? STOP IT! Guess what, I just found the name of the cargo company, it's called "I got your money flight into that airport at whatever time with a box of rocks company"! There really isn't a pot of gold at the end of the rainbow! JUST A THOUGHT!!!

Day Six:

CALLER QUESTION:
Can a disabled person get a discount on the airfare?

RESPONSE:
No, they cannot! Only if you consider being a senior citizen disabled, and what would be your disability—can't talk, can't walk, can't see, can't hear, or just can't think, 'cause for every disabled person that uses the airlines and expects a discount, the airline industry would lose a great deal of revenue, 'cause most of are disabled! JUST A THOUGHT!!!

CALLER QUESTION:
I want to check a flight?

RESPONSE:
What's the airline?
CALLER QUESTION?
XYZ!

RESPONSE:
That's not an airline!

CALLER QUESTION:
Yes, it's XYZ airline!

RESPONSE:
Do you have a flight number?

CALLER QUESTION:
Yes, # 3.

RESPONSE:
(Okay, as you know by now, I'm going along with this for as long as I can take it, and by the sound of this conversation, it won't be long, trust me.) Miss, what's the name of the airline carrier?

CALLER QUESTION:
XYZ airline.

RESPONSE:
I've already looked up the flight going and coming from Tampa, Florida. Coming back to the phone, and at this point I know this woman fell and bumped her head!

CALLER QUESTION:
Oh, I know the airline, it's JetBlue! Did they merge?

RESPONSE:
I must have fallen and bumped my head! The only merge I hear is your mind merging with a satellite in outer space. Your mind is explosive to you and others talking to you! I suggest that you never ever try to fly on an airline again, try Amtrak or Greyhound, 'cause when you look up in the sky it's not just a bird you see; I believe you really think it's Superman! JUST A THOUGHT!!!

CALLER QUESTION:
I want to send a child to Jamaica, the Caribbean island, by himself! How does that work?

RESPONSE:
How old is the child?

CALLER QUESTION:
Four years old.

RESPONSE:
Four years old—you would have to speak with the airline. I don't think the airline will fly a child that young by himself without an adult traveling with him. Okay, people, what is terribly wrong with this call? Have you lost your mind to even have such a dumb idea as this one? On the real, can you imagine if the airline entertained this and allowed your four-year-old on a flight going around the corner by himself? Just think of what a horror story it could be during this flight to Jamaica, in these times; please it's a three-hour flight. Let me share this story about a family that was traveling together: the mother, father, daughter, and sons were going wherever, but when boarding the flight, they couldn't be seated together. The mother and father made some noise 'cause that's not how they booked the flight. However, they settled down and the eleven-year-daughter was seated in the rear of the plane next to a man. The mother and father were seated in the front together, but not first class; all were in coach. The brothers were in the middle of the plane. Maybe an hour into

the flight the mother and father got up and checked on their eleven-year-old daughter. She seemed to be fine, so they returned to their seats. On the approach to landing the man seated next to her had a coat draped over his lap. He then put the coat over her lap and her mouth and began to touch her private parts. When the plane landed, and everyone was ready to depart the plane she started screaming the man was trying to rape her. The brothers, seated closer than the mother and father, dealt with him in a proper way before the police could arrive. I shared that story with this woman to get her to change her mind about sending a four-year-old child on a plane by himself, and after I shared that story with this woman she still wanted to know if it could be done! Perhaps at this point I'm thinking child trafficking, and this isn't her child, hmm! I wish I had my spider senses on for this call, 'cause I would have reported her the proper authorities! JUST A THOUGHT!!!

CALLER QUESTION:
I'm looking for a non-stop flight.

RESPONSE:
Where to?

CALLER QUESTION:
I don't care, I just know I flew last year, and it was non-stop.

RESPONSE:
Okay, what was the name of the airline? And without that information, at least, I can't help you.

CALLER QUESTION:
Do you have a 1-800 number?

RESPONSE:
Yes, but what's the name of the airline?

CALLER QUESTION:
I don't know.

RESPONSE:
Listen, I'm tired of playing tag; let's make this really simple. Hang the phone up and do some research Let your fingers do the walking, which was an old saying—forget the Yellow Pages and look it up. You're probably that person that doesn't have a computer or access to a computer or a smart phone to Google your information. If you can do that the sky will open for you! If not, it's just going to be another cloudy day! JUST A THOUGHT!!!

CALLER QUESTION:
I've been sitting on this plane for six hours.

RESPONSE:
Okay, how can I help you?

CALLER QUESTION:
What happened to the passenger's bill of rights?

RESPONSE:
What rights? Did you mention to the stewardess what is going on, and didn't the pilot make an announcement?

CALLER QUESTION:
Didn't Eliot Spitzer sign a bill for airline passengers to have rights?

RESPONSE:
Sir, I don't know who signed what! And all I'm saying is, ask the stewardess if you can get off the plane!

CALLER QUESTION:
They won't let me get off!

RESPONSE:
Well, this is what I can tell you: ask them to get some scotch, beer, and a glass of wine and get some chips and dip and let it do what it's going to do! Until they correct the problem of taking off or taking the plane back to the gate where you can get off, it's a waiting game!

CALLER QUESTION:
ATTITUDE!!! THANKS FOR NOTHING.

RESPONSE:
You're welcome. People really get this attitude when they're not politically correct; automatically I have an attitude because I'm not giving you what you'd like to hear! Really, you're calling somewhere that can't help you in your current situation but can give you a positive suggestion as to what to do. You had a hard time swallowing that pill; you expected me to say, let me call the pilot of that airline and demand he fly you alone to your destination right now, right now. But really you know how to make this all go away; by investing in your own private jet. And I bet you don't have a clue as to how the airport functions nor do you have knowledge of the FAA rules and regulations, so guess what you still aren't going anywhere! JUST A THOUGHT!!!

CALLER QUESTION:
I'm looking for my son.

RESPONSE:
What airline was he flying?

CALLER QUESTION:
I know the name of the airline; I want to know the time it's landing?

RESPONSE:
It's the same as knowing the name of the airline; they both can change, meaning if he was on a connecting flight that might change the name of the airline and/or the time can change as well!

CALLER QUESTION:
Says never mind…and hangs up!

RESPONSE:
It wasn't important enough to wait and get the right information on your son's flight! Then go kick rocks; maybe the rocks can give you the information you need to meet his flight on time, and when you're not there you will have a lot of explaining to do, Lucy! JUST A THOUGHT!!!

CALLER QUESTION:
Can I have the number to Cathay Pacific airline?

RESPONSE:
Here's the number.

CALLER QUESTION:
Thank you.

RESPONSE:
You're welcome.

CALLER QUESTION:
Now can you give me the number?

RESPONSE:
Did you write the number down when I gave it to you?

CALLER QUESTION:
No, but can you connect me?

RESPONSE:
You first said you wanted the number and I gave it to you, assuming (as you me) that you wrote it down; no mention of connection!

CALLER QUESTION:
Just connect me! Can you connect me to Cathay Pacific airline?

RESPONSE:
What's with this person not taking the number, so this way if there is no answer she won't have to call back; that makes sense

to me! Listen, you refusing to take the number means you're fine with no answer or a constant busy signal. Once either of those things occur while you're trying to connect, don't call back and speak with me, 'cause what you hear may be ugly...so you need to do the right thing and write down this number before I hang up! JUST A THOUGHT!!!

CALLER QUESTION:
I have a complaint about the airport; is this ABC airport or XYZ airport?

RESPONSE:
Yes, this is XYZ airport, how can I help you?

CALLER QUESTION:
I want to know why they left my elderly grandmother in a wheelchair, and she missed her flight!

RESPONSE:
Is XYZ the airport you want or is it ABC airport? Because you need to establish that first before I can help you.

CALLER QUESTION:
It's XYZ airport.

RESPONSE:
Who are they? You said they!

CALLER QUESTION:
I don't know!

RESPONSE:
Again, with the "I don't know"! Why wasn't a family member there to assist her as well as the wheelchair assistant? The airline would have allowed one member of your family to go to the gate with her!

CALLER QUESTION:
My father and uncle were there, but they didn't stay, and they left her.

RESPONSE:
Listen, the airline hires and contracts companies for wheelchair escorts from the ticket counter to the gate and if there are no family members the airline personnel will escort them onto the plane. Does your grandmother speak or understand English?

CALLER QUESTION:
No!

RESPONSE:
This responsibility was solely up to your father or uncle to make sure your grandmother, their mother, would make her flight and not get stranded in a huge airport. The same way somebody asked the airline for a wheelchair they could've asked to get a gate pass, and they should have mentioned that she doesn't speak or understand any English! The nerve you have, to blame the airline for your father and uncle's responsibility to make sure your grandmother got on that plane and not miss her flight. You need to make your complaint to your father and uncle about the horrible way they treated your grandmother! The way I see it, there may some type of insurance involved with this situation; smelling a bit fishy to me! JUST A THOUGHT!!!

Day Seven:

CALLER QUESTION:
I'm shipping a dog on Swiss airline; where do I go to ship the dog?

RESPONSE:
Call this number for Swiss air cargo, then find out what you need and the location.

CALLER QUESTION:
I don't want the number; I want to know where to go, and is it in terminal five?

RESPONSE:
I just love when they ask and answer their questions!

CALLER QUESTION:
How do I carry the dog in the terminal?

RESPONSE:
The dog should be in a kennel, then put on a smart cart, which are outside of the terminal... Now, if you're traveling with another person, someone can park the car in the unloading zone and the other can get the cart, then place the kennel on the smart cart.

CALLER QUESTION:
Do I have to walk to the terminal?

RESPONSE:
Pause for the cause and looking at the phone! Here we go…
No, what you should do is get in the kennel and let the dog put
you on the smart cart and walk you to the terminal! JUST A
THOUGHT!!!

CALLER QUESTION:
I want to go somewhere!

RESPONSE:
Making the assumption that you want to fly, right?

CALLER QUESTION:
I just want prices; do you have numbers or where I can find
prices?

RESPONSE:
No, people, please, again and again I implore you to do some
research on where you'd like to go, the airline you'd like to fly
with, the price you'd like to spend round-trip or one-way on
this trip… These are the basics of flying to and from any airport
around the world or in the States. I guarantee you'd be so satisfied
with the results that you did this all by yourself like adults do,
and you don't have to be off to see the Wizard of Oz because you
need a brain! JUST A THOUGHT!!!

CALLER QUESTION:
Can I have someone paged?

RESPONSE:
What airline?

CALLER QUESTION:
Egypt Air.

RESPONSE:
Here's the number.

CALLER QUESTION:
Is that a nine to five number? Will someone answer?

RESPONSE:
I don't have their schedule as to when they will answer their phones; that's why I gave you the number!

CALLER QUESTION:
The passenger was supposed to be here at three p.m., and we are at the airport terminal and she didn't come out!

RESPONSE:
You're in the terminal? Why didn't you ask someone that works for Egypt Air about the flight? I know if that plane landed on time some of the personnel should still be in the terminal.

CALLER QUESTION:
We can't, they keep telling us to move on!

RESPONSE:
At the beginning of the conversation you didn't mention that there was more than one person in your vehicle, so why didn't one person stay with the vehicle and the other stay outside? May-

be she got her luggage and came down early and she could be outside the baggage area looking for you'll. Why would both of you go in the terminal looking—that's probably how you missed each other. Listen, I don't have time for this cat-and-mouse game; when you two figure it out she is probably home with some popcorn and a movie! JUST A THOUGHT!!!

CALLER QUESTION:
My name is so-and-so; I have a problem! I came from Trinidad on Saturday and there was a problem with my luggage. Customs caused so much confusion; they didn't give me back my passport...who do I speak to about this?

RESPONSE:
Call customs; here's the number!

CALLER QUESTION:
I have that number, and no answer!

RESPONSE:
Sir, relax, I just gave the area code, not the whole number, and you're telling me you have that number...therefore I can't help you! (How dumb is that, jumping out of the basement window with the parachute open.) Perhaps if you had all of the number you would have gotten the answers you need to assist you with your situation, but the race isn't over for you...just stay at that same pace, fast and furious! JUST A THOUGHT!!!

OH, SNOW COME OUT TO PLAY

CALLER QUESTION:
Is the airport open?

RESPONSE:
Yes.

CALLER QUESTION:
Are all the flights being delayed?

RESPONSE:
Pretty much!

CALLER QUESTION:
What kind of delays are the flights experiencing?

RESPONSE:
Hundreds. Where are you calling from?

CALLER QUESTION:
New York.

RESPONSE:
Have you looked out of your window to see how much snow has fallen? Let me give you a little hint…if cars are covered in your area and snow is still falling heavily, then you should say to yourself, Self, look at the weather channel to get a better perspective of what's happening at the airports!

CALLER QUESTION:
Yeah, but I want to know, are there any delays?

RESPONSE:

Are you serious right now? It is so very obvious if there is 12 to 15 inches of snow down at a rapid pace and falling heavily, the airports, railroads, and buses are experiencing some form of delay! I don't know why I'm explaining this to you and you're calling from New York... and you live here. If anyone should know what happens in New York with a major snow storm it should be you! But, I tell you what go outside and see if you can build a snowman that's if you can clear the falling snow out of your doorway. Then see the delay you will experience trying to get back inside you house with the strong freezing wind blowing in your face; and your visibility is almost at zero. Tell me about your delay then; and this is how public transportation runs in this city. Call me back and see the delay you're going to experience by the wait time that I'm going to answer the phone! JUST A THOUGHT!!!

CALLER QUESTION:
I need the address to the airport.

RESPONSE:
There is no physical address to the airport. There's a location. If you have a GPS, put in points of interest, then scroll down to airports—you may have to put in the zip code of the airport—and it will come up with the directions!

CALLER QUESTION:
It doesn't come up with points of interest. What city?

RESPONSE:
Okay, I don't own a GPS device in my vehicle and I don't know which one you have, but anyone else that needed these instructions for their GPS had no problem following them!

CALLER QUESTION:
I know, but what city?

RESPONSE:
This is my last attempt to try to get you to understand my instructions with this GPS thing. People be getting a GPS for gift, for Father's Day, birthdays, Mother's Day, or are just wanting to be in the 21st century with this technology, instead of expecting someone else to help them figure it out while they are driving. First rule of thumb: reading the instructions that came with the apparatus is fundamental. Second: at some point you have to hook it up to your vehicle, then play with it to get the feel for it. It's safe; you can do this at home, children! What happened to your bearings: north, south, east, and west? Either you beat it, or you join it, but whatever you choose, be willing to come into the 21st century and get with the program, don't let the program get you! JUST A THOUGHT!!!

CALLER QUESTION:
I want to change my flight; how do I do that?

RESPONSE:
What airline do you want to change from or to?

CALLER QUESTION:
Uh, Delta.

RESPONSE:
Call Delta at this number, and why wouldn't you know to call the airline you made your reservation with first? What are you afraid of? The worst-case scenario is they tell you that you can't change your flight plans because of the time you decided to do it. Then your reaction is to go into panic mode instantly. Oh no, what should I do…what should I do? You go ahead and pay for another ticket or see if you can get an open-book ticket as long as you give the airline enough time to make that change, but if you waited for the 24th hour, then you buy another ticket, that simple! So, haste will make you waste time! JUST A THOUGHT!!!

CALLER QUESTION:
I'm calling the airport to see if my boyfriend has my car!

RESPONSE:
What do you actually mean? Is it like he took your car and you'll never see him again? Does it mean you saw him drive past your house and didn't stop? Does it mean your girlfriend saw him driving another woman in it? Does it mean you wanted to call him to put up a loaf of bread? Does it mean you were supposed to be going on a trip and he forgot to bring you to the airport? Or does it mean that he came to the airport and parked your vehicle and you want someone to look for your car in the long- and short-term parking lots? What's your angle? I mean, where

is your head right now, 'cause your boyfriend is right next to it and maybe the REPO MAN took it for a ride! You should have made your payments! JUST A THOUGHT!!!

CALLER QUESTION:
I'm from Kenya and I flew into this airport 22 years ago, and I wanted to know if immigration or customs still has my I-90 form to prove I was on a flight from Kenya!

RESPONSE:
Sir, I want you to pay very close attention to what I'm about to say 'cause I'm only going to say this once. I strongly believe that immigration or customs keeps records that far back. Now, if that plane unfortunately crashed, then the FAA and NTSB would have notified the relatives of the passengers as to who was on that plane or not. Real talk, you are in this country for 22 years and are 22 years older—sounds like you need someone to come in and take you around and about, or you were in a very serious accident and are just now coming out of your coma. A lot has changed in 22 years—for instance, those I-90 forms don't exist anymore; everything is done online. My suggestion is to write, FaceTime, Snapchat, email your relative in Kenya and ask them to send you a photo from 22 years ago when you were there, and that should give you all the proof you need to know that you were there and came here on an airline and not a pod! JUST A THOUGHT!!!

CALLER QUESTION:
Phone rings three times.

RESPONSE:
Made proper announcement: company name, then my name, followed up with How may I help you?

CALLER QUESTION:
Oh my God! Are you a real person I'm speaking with?

RESPONSE:
Okay, did anyone get that I announced the company name, then my name, then said, how may I help you? Machines don't do that!

Day Eight:

CALLER QUESTION:
Does the airport have ground transportation to and from airports?

RESPONSE:
Yes, there are shuttle buses that go to and from airports. Here are their numbers.

CALLER QUESTION:
What's that for?

RESPONSE:
The numbers I just provided you are for the shuttle buses that go to and from the airport, as you asked!

CALLER QUESTION:
Oh, so there are buses that do that?

RESPONSE:
Here we go. Why would I give you the names and numbers of shuttle buses that go to and from the airports if you didn't ask for that information, hmm? I just sit here and give people who ask for information pertaining to various things at the airport that they need and give information about how the stock market

is doing and what they should invest their money in! I need to come up with a smelling-salt app through the phone for these people that pass out on me during a conversation. Stay with me, come to the light, Carol Anne, come to the light! JUST A THOUGHT!!!

CALLER QUESTION:
I'm flying Spirit at the airport; do I go up or down?

RESPONSE:
What do you mean?

CALLER QUESTION:
Yeah, departure!

RESPONSE:
Read the signage in front of the airport as you approach the terminals. The upper level is for departure and the lower level is for arrivals of the same terminal.

CALLER QUESTION:
You don't know that!

RESPONSE:
You know, you're right…I just work here, and I've never ever taken a flight from an airport before, unlike you who clearly doesn't know the difference between departures and arrivals at the terminals. Perhaps these words are too complicated for you to understand, so my suggestion is, don't come into the

airport until you stand at the beginning of the airport and read the signs that say, "departures upper level" and "arrivals lower level." This is your homework assignment. A test will be given the next time you try to do this without reading, because you are wasting other people's valuable time. Know the difference between departures and arrivals; MOVE GET OUT THE WAY! JUST A THOUGHT!!!

CALLER QUESTION:
I need to know if someone at the airport can change my tire on my car! I'm in California and won't be back for another two weeks, and when I parked my vehicle and got out I noticed I had a flat tire on my front left side, so can someone go and change it?

RESPONSE:
No, you have to be here and call the towing company and tell them where you and your vehicle are in the parking lot and the details of your car, such as make and model and color, so they can assist you.

CALLER QUESTION:
I thought I could give them my credit card information and they could go do it!

RESPONSE:
That's like if you had service done to your vehicle and you were there and gave a credit card, you would still have to sign, correct?

CALLER QUESTION:

(Remark of the caller.) Welcome to New York.

RESPONSE:
No, welcome to common sense! JUST A THOUGHT!!!

CALLER QUESTION:
I have a question as to what I can bring on the plane?

RESPONSE:
I get a zillion of these questions every day, but with different situations attached! What's your question?

CALLER QUESTION:
I have a passport; can I bring it with me to Puerto Rico?

RESPONSE:
Why would you? You don't need a passport to go to Puerto Rico; it's a territory of the United States…and when traveling in the United States you don't need a passport. What is needed is a state-issued ID. What I need from you is some research and understanding about the United States and its regions of other states and territories it has, and for you to educate yourself so the next time this conversation comes up you'll know about Puerto Rico and the United States for your sake; learn something today! JUST A THOUGHT!!!

Day Nine:

CALLER QUESTION:
I'm traveling with an infant and my fourteen-year-old son; my question is, I have a stroller for my infant; what can I do with it?

RESPONSE:
You can do one of two things with the stroller. If it's important to have the stroller when you get off the plane, then when you check in to the ticket counter tell that to the ticket agent. Then you go through TSA screening with the stroller and the stewardess will place it securely in front of the plane. Two, if it's not imperative for you to have the stroller when you get off the plane, then check it in. Truth be told, I personally would have them put the stroller on the plane instead of checking it in, 'cause how they handle the luggage is scary enough. The stroller wouldn't stand a chance, coming on the baggage belt looking like it's all broken up, and I know those strollers aren't cheap! JUST A THOUGHT!!!

CALLER QUESTION:
I have a lot of questions to ask, but it seems like you're in a hurry to get me off the phone...so I want to speak to someone else. I've been hanging on this phone waiting for 16 minutes for someone to answer my questions!

RESPONSE:
Let's get it on… First of all, the phone hasn't rung for 16 minutes and no one answered. Second, why would somebody stay on a phone letting it ring in their ear for these so-called 16 minutes—nobody I know would! Third, if you are really focused on getting your questions answered, you should be listening to things that are being answered pertaining to the questions asked. Fourth, it wouldn't be more than and would probably be less than 5 minutes to answer most questions asked by customers; maybe a little more, but not 16 minutes! And fifth but not least, you made it seem like 16 minutes you waited on the phone 'cause once I spoke with you all I heard was a hmm, a hmm, a hmm, and by the time you got to one of the many of your so-called questions it was 16 minutes. What you need to do in future endeavors is, write down your questions so when a person in customer service answers the phone ready for you, you'll be ready for them; it's like going to the grocery store to shop: write down the things you need, go get them, and come out of the store satisfied 'cause you got everything you needed. JUST A THOUGHT!!!

CALLER QUESTION:
I have a relative coming in August; I want to know, is there a metro card machine in the airport?

RESPONSE:
Yes, when going toward the train station.

CALLER QUESTION:
Are they in the airport?

RESPONSE:

Yes, again answering a repetitive question! Listen, I've given you all the information that pertains to your situation with the MetroCard machines. I'm pretty sure that your relative can speak up for him or herself to ask for a MetroCard machine in the terminal and the train station, because there are numerous employed personnel here in both areas to assist your relative, so have no fear, the metro card machines will be there! JUST A THOUGHT!!!

CALLER QUESTION:

Is the airport open?

RESPONSE:

Why wouldn't it be?

CALLER QUESTION:

It's raining and I'm checking!

RESPONSE:

Okay, and "it's raining" meaning what again? Do you have a flight to catch, are you expecting a relative or friend—it can't be that you just want to check...if that's your problem for the day then you're in a sad state of affairs. Go outside, I'll hold on, and stand in the rain to see how long it would take you to get soaking wet or realize that you need an umbrella. Now, did that stop you from continuing on with your day? That applies the same for the airplanes: they get wet but keep on flying until that big umbrella comes out and keeps them dry! JUST A THOUGHT!!!

Day Ten:

CALLER QUESTION:
How much would it cost to ship a bird from Wisconsin?

RESPONSE:
I don't know, but where in Wisconsin is the bird flying from and do you have a flight number or time?

CALLER QUESTION:
Maybe Delhi or Bombay, India. I don't remember. (Caller says hold on.) Caller comes back and says it's Delhi and the flight were supposed to be here at 6:53 a.m.

RESPONSE:
The flight with that time from Delhi has landed, and it was on time.

CALLER QUESTION:
Caller repeats, it came in on time at 6:53 a.m.

RESPONSE:
Yes, which means it has landed on time at 6:53 a.m.

CALLER QUESTION:
It arrived?!

RESPONSE:
Look, I can't be clearer than telling you now for the third time that the flight came in on time, and believe it or not, these flights come in on time more times than not, 'cause this is a business that prides itself on doing that or being penalized when they aren't on time, understand? As far as I'm concerned, I think you are the one who flew over the cuckoo's nest! JUST A THOUGHT!!!

CALLER QUESTION:
I need three airline numbers.

RESPONSE:
What are the airlines?

CALLER QUESTION:
I don't know yet, but can you give me three numbers or not?

RESPONSE:
I can give you 43 numbers to airlines if you tell me what airline numbers you need, and why do you need three? And what do you need—to make reservations, baggage, flight information, or what? Can you help me help you?

CALLER QUESTION:
I want to book a flight.

RESPONSE:
You need reservation numbers, but you haven't told me what airlines you would like...and if you don't know that you need,

let your finger do the walking and get the Yellow Pages out and start looking. Close your eyes and turn your index finger around and place it on the page, then see what airline it is and call them with the context, 'cause actually you're wasting your time and mine! JUST A THOUGHT!!!

CALLER QUESTION:
I'm calling to find out what airline my mother is flying with?

RESPONSE:
What airline is she flying, the name of the airline!

CALLER QUESTION:
Terminal 5...is it open?

RESPONSE:
Yes, it's open, but what is your interest in terminal 5...is that the terminal your mother is coming into?

CALLER QUESTION:
Oh, okay. Caller hangs up!

RESPONSE:
Really, there is nothing better to with your day than call an airport and inquire about someone and then turn to information about a terminal and then hang up? Mental illness is so very prevalent in this country that it's sad we can't get this under control! JUST A THOUGHT!!!

CALLER QUESTION:
I'm calling for a Pakistani airline number.

RESPONSE:
Yes, here's the number.

CALLER QUESTION:
I have been waiting for a half hour calling that number.

RESPONSE:
That has something to do with the Pakistani airline, not here. It's 7 a.m. here and my eyes are hardly open, let alone looking for the right number. I know I did though, so why are you calling here again? Maybe the staff at the number is not open yet to answer the phone. I answered because this is the time I start working, but I can't answer any of your questions, and if I call the same number I gave you I'm going to get the same answer: none. You do know they have a cell phone for seniors; it has big numbers, so they can dial their families and you can even program the number for them, so in this case you can call them and find out what's happening! This is the dawning of the day of Aquarius, the day of Aquarius! JUST A THOUGHT!!!

CALLER QUESTION:
My friend is traveling from terminal 11 to terminal 14, how do they do that?

RESPONSE:
They have get to the air train that goes to each terminal.

CALLER QUESTION:
How often do they run?

RESPONSE:
Every two to three minutes.

CALLER QUESTION:
Oh, that often?

RESPONSE:
Yes.

CALLER QUESTION:
So, he just gets on the train and goes to the terminal he needs? On the Web it's saying the terminal 11 is closed!

RESPONSE:
No, terminal 11 is open.

CALLER QUESTION:
I know it's not because I've traveled in it the past month!

RESPONSE:
So, if you traveled in that terminal last month and I told you it is open, why are we still talking about a web page? What does that have to do with your friend and the air train to the terminals? Let me make this part of this conversation quite clear: I don't have any more time in my meter to give you. If your friend needs information about the air train, your suggestion and good deed

for the day is to tell him to call himself and get the information he needs to get from one terminal to the next. Surely if he gets it from you he'll be stuck like Chuck! JUST A THOUGHT!!!

CALLER QUESTION:
How you doing? My grandmother was taken to the airport to get on a flight from Pennsylvania to Florida. She suffers from chronic Alzheimer's and I'm at the airport waiting for her.

RESPONSE:
What airline was she flying with, do you know?

CALLER QUESTION:
Hmm, not sure, could you help, please?

RESPONSE:
How in the hell am I going to help you if you can't help yourself? You should be ashamed of yourself for telling this story to someone. Oh, just lost my chronically ill suffering-from-Alzheimer's grandmother traveling by herself in a huge airport at 10 p.m., can you help me find her? And I'm in Florida waiting but she didn't get off the plane! Call lost and found; she might be sitting there waiting for someone to put her up! JUST A THOUGHT!!!

Day Eleven:

CALLER QUESTION:
Hello, I'm calling for lost and found.

RESPONSE:
For what airline?

CALLER QUESTION:
ANA.

RESPONSE:
Call this number; it's lost and found for the airline.

CALLER QUESTION:
Is it at the airport?

RESPONSE:
Yes, the number is for the airline lost and found...or my real response goes like this: No, that's not the number for the airline lost and found; it's for Motel 6! Why don't you wait a while, let the information you just received sink in before sounding crazy...why make it so hard for yourself? Pay attention and keep it moving, soldier! JUST A THOUGHT!!!

CALLER QUESTION:
I'm calling about a letter that customs sent me, and the letter said for me to call the airport!

RESPONSE:
DON'T ADJUST YOUR CHANNEL. THERE IS NOTHING WRONG WITH THE TELEVISION; IT'S JUST THAT YOU HAVE ENTERED INTO THE TWILIGHT ZONE!!!... Why would customs send you a letter stating that you need to call the airport?

CALLER QUESTION:
I don't know, is this ISOC?

RESPONSE:
Never heard of ISOC, and they gave you this number for what? And that's impossible, 'cause this number has no connection to customs and we are not allowed to give the customs number to the public like that. From the sound of it it's a scam!

CALLER QUESTION:
You people suck up there?

RESPONSE:
No, I think you still have that big lollipop, and you're the sucker here... You are so desperate to believe that you're getting something for nothing you've convinced yourself that someone from somewhere sent you a letter saying you won one million dollars; oh, that's right, it was customs sending you this letter. You're dumb as a doorknob if you believe this, but I'll tell you what, I'll be your pen pal too, and when I send you a letter about one

million dollars, you call me back and I'll tell you where to go and put it up! JUST A THOUGHT!!!

CALLER QUESTION:
I'm expecting to leave on a flight today, but I found out that the airline is leaving 45 minute late. So, will I be 45 minutes late to New York?

RESPONSE:
I would think it would have some effect on your arrival time.

CALLER QUESTION:
So, what should I do and where can I park?

RESPONSE:
When you come into the airport, follow the sign that says parking. Once you're in the terminal and checked in, then look at the flight board and see if the time has changed for your flight. What I suggest is that you make that flight and hope the pilot can make up some of that time, 'cause calling this number and saying the status hasn't changed means nothing to me. It's not like I can call the pilot and say, Look, you're already 45 minutes late on departure, can you put the pedal to the metal and let it all hang out! JUST A THOUGHT!!!

Day Twelve:

CALLER QUESTION:
I'm calling to find out about a package at the airport.

RESPONSE:
What package, and who sent the package, and where did they send the package to at the airport?

CALLER QUESTION:
I've called FedEx and they said they didn't have the package.

RESPONSE:
Okay, what company has your package?

CALLER QUESTION:
The airport.

RESPONSE:
No, this is just an airport and this part is information for the airport. Now, what cargo company are you looking for?

CALLER QUESTION:
Can you connect me to a company that handles cargo?

RESPONSE:
Again, there is no one cargo company handling all packages coming into this airport; you have to have an airway bill or a tracking number, something!

CALLER QUESTION:
Try FedEx.

RESPONSE:
Didn't you just tell me you called FedEx and they told you that they didn't have a package for you? And besides, you don't have any information for them to look for your package. Listen, this is taking too much of my time looking for some package that you've made up your mind the airport has! Let's make a deal: do you think it's in door 1, 2, or 3? I'll make your decision easier for you—how about you take all three packages, because you just received a package of rocks. There is no package here at the airport for you! Tell you what, why don't you wrap up a package and address it to yourself and put on it "from airport"? I mean, whatever floats your boat or moves your canoe! JUST A THOUGHT!!!

CALLER QUESTION:
Hello, I'm calling to see if the airport has phone booths?

RESPONSE:
Uh!

CALLER QUESTION:
I want to know, when I get off the plane, can I make a phone call in the terminal at a phone booth?

RESPONSE:
Yes, miss, the terminals have phone booths, but they're not coin-operated, you need a credit card!

CALLER QUESTION:

So, they do have phone booths, 'cause I don't own a cell phone!

RESPONSE:

Yes, most airports have phone booths in the terminals, but the reality is coin phone booths are obsolete and credit cards are required to use a public phone at the airport . And that's what I told you; you have to have a credit card to use the phone in the terminals. Or you can make a fire and send up smoke signals! Hello, hello, can you hear me now! JUST A THOUGHT!!!

Day Thirteen:

CALLER QUESTION:
I want to know, if I'm picking up someone from the terminal, can I meet them in departures?

RESPONSE:
Why would you want to meet someone in departures when they are coming on an arrivals flight?

CALLER QUESTION:
It gets too crowded in the arrivals area!

RESPONSE:
Yeah, mainly because people are landing and picking up their luggage and meeting family and friends in that area!

CALLER QUESTION:
They say it's a mile to walk from the parking lot to the terminal.

RESPONSE:
I don't know who they are, but what I do know is, parking is directly across from the terminal in walking distance to the terminal, and I do know if you park your vehicle in front of the terminal it will be towed!

CALLER QUESTION:
Can't you drop off and pick up passengers?

RESPONSE:
This is taking way too long for you not to get the gist of this conversation, so this is how I'm going to break down for you... If you want to pick up someone that's arriving, you go directly to the arrivals area and you'll see the person you are waiting for come out to get their luggage. If you try to wait in front of the terminal, you will be asked to move; if not you will be towed! But who am I to tell you what to do at this airport to make your experience a bit easier to navigate the terminals and parking lots—after all, you called me for information; I didn't call you. Maybe your friend comes into the arrivals area and gets his luggage and runs out, then goes upstairs to meet you in departure for your flight, I don't know! You'd better make more dollars, because you're not making any sense right now! JUST A THOUGHT!!!

CALLER QUESTION:
Can you give me the number to the airport cargo?

RESPONSE:
There is no one cargo company number at the airport.

CALLER QUESTION:
I have an invoice number, but I don't know how to find it on the invoice!

RESPONSE:
It should have the name of the company and the invoice number should be on the top of the invoice try looking on the top right corner.

CALLER QUESTION:
It says Futu from Thailand.

RESPONSE:
That's not here at the airport; perhaps it could be a company outside of the airport, and if so we may not have that number.

CALLER QUESTION:
So, do you have a number for cargo?

RESPONSE:
Now, I don't know what part of the sentence you didn't get…you need the name of the cargo company or you need to try to contact the company that shipped you whatever. Please, again, this isn't rocket science, and you're not trying to solve the equation of how many times the planets revolve around the sun . You need to look at that invoice very carefully and find a phone number; even if it's overseas you have to call. But you really need to stop doing business overseas and keep it here in the USA, you're not ready for the truth! JUST A THOUGHT!!!

Day Fourteen:

CALLER QUESTION:
Hey, I'm calling to get my taxes back on a buddy pass ticket!

RESPONSE:
What! (Okay, people, for those who don't know what buddy passes are, they are standby passes given by an airline personnel members for family and friends, which means you have to wait until some paid passenger cancels their flight or the flight isn't filled up. Then you as a buddy pass flier go on the plane. And you may have to wait several flights until you can get on a flight. Now I'm going to get back to this person who has a buddy pass for a flight.) First of all, the airline doesn't have a policy that when you purchase a ticket it has some tax refund attached to it. Secondly, that buddy pass you got from someone working for the airline is for free, and it too has no tax refund attached to it.

CALLER QUESTION:
What do you mean? I need my taxes back on this buddy pass; they did it before without a problem!

RESPONSE:
Sir, if this was done before, why aren't you talking to whoever did it before for you? Hold on. (I'm calling the airline and connecting him to the airline and listening in; in case I get another call

like this I'll know what to say. The airline representative answers and the man proceeds with his question. Representative: tells him the airline has nothing to do with tax refunds on buddy passes or purchased tickets and perhaps he should speak with the person he got the pass from). Representative: How long did you have the pass? Is it more than a year? Caller: It's been more than a year. Representative: It may be a problem, because I think they only last for up to a year.

CALLER QUESTION:
Yes, it's been more than a year, and I can't speak with the person who gave me the buddy pass, 'cause he had a bad stroke and can't talk or write! Representative: Again, there's nothing that we as the airline can do for you. Perhaps you can bring the buddy pass to the airline at the airport and see what happens, but, truthfully, if it's been more than a year I really wouldn't waste your time.

RESPONSE:
Come on, man, really, you can't be serious right now about this tax thing on something you didn't even buy; someone gave you something for free. This isn't a department-store purchase where you bought clothing or whatever and you wanted to return it and get your taxes and your refund back; these are airline tickets. Imagine if every airline did that type of business! Picture this multi-billion-dollar industry not making money! GOING OUT OF BUSINESS, 100% off all flights and buddy passes, and all tax refunds are given back! JUST A THOUGHT!!!

CALLER QUESTION:
Give me the number for customs at ABC airport.

RESPONSE:
There is no customs or immigration at ABC, because it's a domestic airport! XYZ yes, 'cause it's an international airport.

CALLER QUESTION: I'm going to Canada.

RESPONSE:
Okay, you should clear customs in Canada!

CALLER QUESTION:
I want the TSA number, because on the Internet that's who stamps your passport, so you should check the Internet!

RESPONSE:
I don't have to check the Internet to know if you're coming from Canada from ABC airport, which you aren't, TSA doesn't stamp any passport or anything else. For your information, TSA means transportation security administration, not customs. But you know, what might even be better is if you stay on the Canadian side and don't bother with these conflicting situations! JUST A THOUGHT!!!

CALLER QUESTION:
I'm calling about my brother's items lost in terminal JB.

RESPONSE:
Okay, I remember giving you the number you needed for your situation earlier!

CALLER QUESTION:
Yeah, I spoke to JB and they said they didn't have his items and to call the airport!

RESPONSE:
I gave you the number for JB at the airport.

CALLER QUESTION:
No, you didn't, because I called at 5 p.m.

RESPONSE:
Here's where it's about to go crazy! You called at 5 p.m., and what does that mean? Is that when I spoke with you and gave you the number?

CALLER QUESTION:
No, you didn't give me a number!

RESPONSE:
You said you spoke to JB already, and they told you to call the airport! Listen to me, I'm not about to go back and forth with this, I'm not, so pay very, very close attention to what I'm about to say! The number that I know I gave you twice is the number here in the airport. It's the JB terminal number and that's the only number for lost items with their airline. Another suggestion I have for you is, let the person whose items were lost on the flight call for themselves, and keep your day job 'cause a private investigator you're not! JUST A THOUGHT!!!

Day Fifteen:

CALLER QUESTION:
I'm calling about me missing five pairs of pants from my luggage.

RESPONSE:
Wait a minute, did you call here before?

CALLER QUESTION:
Yeah, yesterday.

RESPONSE:
Twice, I gave you the number to call! What happened?

CALLER QUESTION:
I called that number and they said call this number.

RESPONSE:
Whoever they are didn't tell you to call this number, because this number doesn't handle luggage complaints for the airline; the airline does. You really need to call the number given to you and stop making up stories over the phone, and yours is even well enough to listen to, so stop wasting time with charades and go to the men's store and buy five more pairs of pants. Goodwill has nice clothing; maybe you can get your five pairs of pants from them! JUST A THOUGHT!!!

Dorinda Henderson

THE TIME WHEN THIS CALL CAME IN WAS 10 p.m.:

CALLER QUESTION:
I want the number for people who screen your luggage!

RESPONSE:
That would be the TSA, and what airport are you referring to?

CALLER QUESTION:
ABC, here's what happened…TSA went through my luggage and then opened my luggage and took my laptop. They almost made me miss my flight when they finished. I was putting my things back together and they didn't give me back my laptop!

RESPONSE:
They didn't give you back your laptop? How about you telling TSA to give you back your laptop, cause you saw when they removed it from your luggage!

CALLER QUESTION:
Oh, you're one of those people who don't forget and are so perfect!

RESPONSE:
No, ma'am, I'm neither. I'm just mindful of what I'm doing and where I'm doing it, and of who is doing it. If for whatever reason TSA felt they needed to put hands on my laptop, I know they better have put it back. And even before it had gotten to that point I would have said something, so that wouldn't have

happened if it were my laptop. If they wanted to see it and have me open it, okay, done, but them physically taking it and not giving it back, not happening.

CALLER QUESTION:
I'm from New York and I know what goes on!

RESPONSE:
Meaning what? What I think it could mean is that you should be a little more vigilant about your surroundings and protect your property no matter where you're at in the city!

CALLER QUESTION:
Okay, I don't need to be lectured, you're right…so who do I speak to about this? I called a number and there was a recording saying the office will be open at 10 a.m., please leave your name and number and the reason for the call and someone will get back to you.

RESPONSE:
Let me check my numbers and compare your number to see if they are the same.

CALLER QUESTION:
That's not the number I dialed.
TIME NOW IS 10:20 p.m.

RESPONSE:
The number I'm trying is out of order, and I called operations three times to get another number for TSA lost and found, and that was a recording. Returning back to the caller: Hello, call

the first number back and follow the instructions and if no one answers, then try in the morning.

CALLER QUESTION:
You mean to tell me there is no one at the airport to talk to now?

RESPONSE:
Unfortunately, not, or they have flights going out and can be busy. I'm not trying to make any excuses for them, just giving some probabilities. Like I said, keep trying that number and hopefully someone will put up and be able to help you! But in the near future, keep your eyes on the prize and never let them see you sweat! JUST A THOUGHT!!!

Day Sixteen:

This call has been mentioned earlier in the book. What is wrong with this call was, you asked, then answered your own question in English. How unfortunate that you don't have the courage to speak English for a few minutes, so you can receive information that you wanted about an airline. How unfortunate that you're here in this country for however long, receiving all the benefits this country has to offer to you and your family, and you feelin it not necessary to speak its main language... I say shame on you! You've been here so long that you have to get a child to speak English for you, so you can get the information you need... I say shame on you! Look, don't get me wrong, I'm not saying that you have to always speak English, but you need information and that person, me, only speaks English; you should be able to speak that. All the airport information you need is in the terminal, the airline phone number, and the estimated time of arrival (ETA). JUST A THOUGHT!!!

CALLER QUESTION:
Hey, my wife called me and told me she missed her flight, and she is nine months pregnant and not feeling well. They told her she has a long walk to the gate in the terminal. Will there be someone that can help her?

RESPONSE:
She should've asked for assistance when she checked into the ticket counter.

CALLER QUESTION:
Caller interrupted and said, she told me no one was around.

RESPONSE:
What airport is she in?

CALLER QUESTION:
XYZ and her flight was at 8:35 a.m. and she said she was there at 8:30 a.m.!

RESPONSE:
Well, well, well, that's the reason she missed her flight, because she was there five minutes before the flight. This is very important message people. TIME, TIME, TIME is crucial for the airline business. You must be in the check-in line at least two to three hours before your flight. It's not like the airline just has you standing in line for nothing just to see how you can stand without complaining, things are going on, like checking people in with their luggage, answering questions, making sure their itinerary is correct. Then comes the unique experience with TSA; that's more time-consuming and creates long lines and taking off shoes and placing all your metal belongings in a basket. So what airline terminal is your wife in?

CALLER QUESTION:
18.

RESPONSE:
What! 18 is the gate number in the terminal. This is what people don't get, and it's really simple like Sunday morning! You need all the information you need when the reservation was made, no more and no less; just keep it simple!

CALLER QUESTION:
That's all she gave me!

RESPONSE:
God please forgive me, but if something more were to happen to your wife and the only information you have is a gate number at an international airport and you're calling from Virginia, this is truly sad and disgusting to say the least! Then you want to blame the entire airport and airline and everyone that works at the airport for your wife not being here in time for her flight! Truth be told, your wife stressed herself out by not complying with the rules of the airline and being here in a timely fashion. You need to call your wife and calm her down before she gives birth to your child in the terminal, and then you can name it TIME! JUST A THOUGHT!!!

Day Seventeen:

CALLER QUESTION:
Hello, I want to know, what time do the stores open up in the terminal for buying liquor?

RESPONSE:
They open about 10 a.m. or 11 a.m.

CALLER QUESTION:
I want to know, because I want a drink!131

RESPONSE:
I know there aren't any liquor stores open that early.

CALLER QUESTION:
Do you have a number I can call?

RESPONSE:
No, but I do know there is nothing open before the times I mentioned.

CALLER QUESTION:
I'm coming to the airport at 4 a.m.

RESPONSE:
Definitely nothing open at that time, again (repetitive question).

CALLER QUESTION:
I want to buy some Champagne and my flight leaves at 6 a.m. Are you sure nothing is open at that time?

RESPONSE:
Sir, no liquor store is open at 4 a.m. or 6 a.m. in the morning, even in your neighborhood. Okay, this person really doesn't get it, so let me break this one down for you. If you really need a drink that bad, why don't you drink about 2 a.m. or 3 a.m. before you get to the airport? But be mindful that you have a flight to catch, so you don't want to be too intoxicated, because they won't let you on the flight. Another suggestion is, you raise your right or left hand and say MY NAME IS! JUST A THOUGHT!!!

CALLER QUESTION:
I'm calling to find out about shots given when you go out of the country; does the airport have a medical facility that provides this service?

RESPONSE:
Yes, there is a number I can give, please hold on! I still can hear the person talking after I said hold on!

CALLER QUESTION:
If you have a number, can I tell them?

RESPONSE:
Yes, again, I have a number, but they relocated. Are you familiar with the area? Here's the address for the medical building.

CALLER QUESTION:
Is that in the area I'm in?

RESPONSE:
 Some people can't multitask and when trying to do so, your mind says your starting to take in new information about your flight when you called the airport. Then here it comes distraction and then at that moment your mind shuts down and says OVERLOAD OVERLOAD ABORT ABORT MISSION. This is why I say to some people, FOCUS ON YOUR GOALS AND MISSION FOR YOUR CALL, at least for the time being. That's the main reason for calling information, to obtain it. Are you smarter than a fifth grader! JUST A THOUGHT!!!

Day Eighteen:

CALLER QUESTION:
Good morning, madam, can you tell me where gate B-20 at Northwest airline is?

RESPONSE:
I don't know physically where gate B-20 in Northwest terminal is, because I don't work in the terminal. It is to your right or to your left. Are you in Northwest terminal now?

CALLER QUESTION:
Oh no, I'm not the passenger; I'm calling on behalf of my client. This is MasterCard and my customer wanted me to find out the location in the terminal.

RESPONSE:
When your customer calls back for that information, and when they get into Northwest terminal and check in, that's when they find out the gate assignment and ask the ticket agent which way it is to the gate. Let me understand you here: you're a representative of MasterCard and you are calling airport information?

CALLER QUESTION:
I agree, but do you know?

RESPONSE:
Whatever that means! It doesn't make sense to have this confusion in one's world. Show a little common sense—I have to find a bathroom in the terminal and I'll call MasterCard, then they'll call me, the customer, back and give me the bathroom location over the phone. I'm going to take a guess, but I think there are so many employees and passengers in any given terminal that you can be up close and personal to ask where bathroom is in the terminal. It's just a terminal at the airport, people, not Jurassic park! JUST A THOUGHT!!!

CALLER QUESTION:
I have a complaint; there were heavy plane sounds all last night in my area.

RESPONSE:
I'm listening.

CALLER QUESTION:
Yes.

RESPONSE:
Hold on, please, for a number! You know, I can understand the noise that some make when going over a house because you live in the binding pattern of the flight, but planes don't fly all night. And if for whatever reason the flight pattern may have changed, that's the FAA you call and no one else. Look, there is a first time for everything, so face it, when you purchased the house, apartment, townhouse, or condo, you should have asked the realtor, is

this in the path of planes landing? Should I get earplugs or turn up the music loud? It's the way it is and that's what it is, but a change is coming, wait for it! JUST A THOUGHT!!!

CALLER QUESTION: Hi, my daughter, who is sixteen, has a flight, and I'm assuming it's terminal one. How would she get there? And where is terminal one?

RESPONSE:
You asked and then answered your own question, but she can take the air train that goes to terminal one, right!

CALLER QUESTION:
No, I know that, but how is she getting to her connection at terminal 3?

RESPONSE:
Take the air train that goes to each terminal in the airport.

CALLER QUESTION:
The air train will take her to the terminal?

RESPONSE:
Silence; again, answering your own question!

CALLER QUESTION:
Okay, thank you!

RESPONSE:
Stop trying to be so correct at all the time—just ask the question; it saves a lot of time and the answer is equally short. And lose the

attitudes! And all of what you think you know, and you don't, the listener gets a bit bored and confused, because you're all over the place with your questions. Can you "cut to the chase meaning get to your point of this call. There is no need to give all the in-depth details of what you think you know! Just the facts, ma'am, just the facts: it's only a transfer from terminal to terminal, not from Mars, Jupiter, Venus, then Brooklyn and back! KISS (keep it simple, stupid). JUST A THOUGHT!

Day Nineteen:

CALLER QUESTION:
Hello, this Dr. Whoever and I'm calling to speak to someone at your medical department. The reason being, I have some patients calling in on various airlines to your airport and they asked if I can provide fake certificates for meningitis; this certificate would prove that they were given meningitis shots before entering the United States!

RESPONSE:
Hold on, please; I'll transfer this call to our medical facility.

CALLER QUESTION:
Doctor identifies himself and explains the situation . He states one of his patient is traveling out of the country; and after seeing the patient he noticed his prescription pad had been stolen from office. He believes the vaccination certificate they received is fake as well. He says that's how they do it in India. He told them they wasn't in India and he wouldn't issue a certificate like unless they got their shots. The doctor believes they received a certificate from another doctor and he is very concerned about this situation, because if these people came into the United States with meningitis untreated the result would be a full-blown, widespread, deadly epidemic. He gave information on the name

of the airline, the time, and where they were traveling from. He gave his phone number and urged the person he was speaking with to have someone call him back within the next two hours to let him know about the certificate, and whether it was real or fake. He faxed a description of what the certificate should look like in order to get your meningitis shots. He said it was of great importance that they passed this information to the proper authorities immediately and turned these people back around. And if the proper authorities called, I could answer as many questions as possible without giving the patient medical information out, but to confirm whether their immunization shots were given or not.

RESPONSE:
This is serious; what if this doctor didn't have this number to call and inform me of this situation, then what? These people, like so many others have gotten into this country without proper paperwork or vaccinations and are moving about spreading this deadly disease amongst many people they come into contact with. Listen, we have enough medical problems in this country to speak of without having any more, e.g., the flu strand, which is a virus and not a disease, but now it's gone from regular flu to H1N1 flu in this country, and there are a host of other viruses and diseases that I can't begin to mention that have slipped into this country. Suggestion: stay in your country until you are properly vaccinated to come into ours; show more pride and dignity coming into this country! This has been one of the many problems this country has faced and just letting anybody in poses a threat to our health. If these people want to come to the land of the free they need to act like it and do the right thing. Opportunity and freedom come to those that earn it and follow

the rules and the law of this land and are seeking a better life for them and their family. They say this is supposed to be equal opportunity for all, but I say that live here first; I really don't see the benefits of letting people into this country that are sick, have very little education and no job skills, and can't speak English enough to understand them. There is so much unfinished business here with our people living in the United States; I don't see the need to take on anyone else that isn't able to contribute to this country. Ellis Island comes to mind; when people migrated here doctors were there before they got off that ship, checking the healthy and sick. If they were fit and able to conclude the process then they were allowed into this country, and the ones that weren't healthy enough were sent back, and the reason why the healthy ones were allowed to stay was because they were able to work and contribute. What I'm saying is, when you come to someone's house for the first time, bring something to the table, to coin a phrase! JUST A THOUGHT!!!

CALLER QUESTION:
We're stuck on the road to the airport; actually, the road is shut down. Can I call the airline and find out if the plane will be delayed because of this?

RESPONSE:
Let me be clear, the airline will not delay any flight departing because of a road closure to the airport. If the airline was having problems on the runway or taxiway there may be a delay, but that's the only time that would occur.

CALLER QUESTION:
What if no one flies the plane or no one boards the plane, would they still fly?

RESPONSE:
WHAT!! Okay, the chance that no one will be on board a flight is not very likely. Here we go: I tell you to be at the airport two to three hours in advance so that gives you time for any unforeseen occurrences to happen, like a shuttle from Mars came down and wanted me to test the atmosphere, or we missed the cab 'cause they put up another fare, or whatever might make you late for your flight, be prepared. But I can tell you this: everyone that's on that same flight you wanted to be delayed wasn't on that same road that was closed to the airport, I bet you that! JUST A THOUGHT!!!

CALLER QUESTION:
You're right, can I get another number to another airline to see if I can make new reservations?

RESPONSE:
I liked this talk; finally, I think someone got it! Yes, here is a number to the airline, message received, hallelujah! JUST A THOUGHT!!!

CALLER QUESTION:
I have a couple of questions; I don't know if you can help me. Could you verify the directions that I have, because I'm coming from South Jersey?

RESPONSE:
Okay.

CALLER QUESTION:
Yeah, I'm coming from South Jersey and I don't know if you could help me with this!

RESPONSE:
What is this? You aren't giving me any questions for me to help you with; you just keep repeating yourself!

CALLER QUESTION:
Oh yeah, I'm coming from South Jersey and using the Goethals Bridge.

RESPONSE:
Staten Island Expressway, Verrazano Bridge, Belt Parkway East, you'll see signs for XYZ airport.

CALLER QUESTION:
I have a GPS; what's the address?

RESPONSE:
Okay, readers, look at my face if you can imagine it! What do you think my response is going to be with this one? This is your quiz; I'm going to let my readers figure this one out. It's an open-book quiz and whatever comes to your minds I'll accept and give everyone a passing grade! JUST A THOUGHT!!!

Day Twenty:

CALLER QUESTION:
I need a number to an airline; I'm looking for someone who landed last night at 11 p.m.

RESPONSE:
What's the name of the airline?

CALLER QUESTION:
Gives me the name of airline.

RESPONSE:
I give the number to the airline and say that this particular airline doesn't come into the airport until later in the day, and that you should try calling periodically throughout the day!

CALLER QUESTION:
Hangs up! Calls again with the same information!

RESPONSE:
Didn't I just speak with you and give you a number?

CALLER QUESTION:
Yeah, but no one answered!

RESPONSE:

Didn't I just explain to you why no one may be at the terminal yet and to keep trying throughout the day? Here goes the crazy with this call: you were expecting someone that allegedly landed at 11 p.m. last night and it's 7 a.m. the next day; then you want to speak to someone from the airline to verify this information. News flash: you're really wasting your time if you think the airline is going to tell you whether that person was on that flight at all. How well do you know this person not to have a number to call them at? But you know how the saying goes: "It's the early bird that catches the worm"! JUST A THOUGHT!!!

CALLER QUESTION:

What do I have to show airport security before I get on the plane? I had prostate surgery and they gave me a bag for my urine that goes around my leg!

RESPONSE:

Do you have a doctor's note or discharge papers from the hospital stating your condition?

CALLER QUESTION:

They didn't give me any discharge papers; they kept them!

RESPONSE:

You let a doctor do surgery in a hospital and the nurse didn't give you any discharge papers or instructions and prescriptions the doctor signed off on? They just let you walk out of the hospital and didn't sign any discharge papers? C'MON, MAN, I'm not buying that, and I know for a fact that's not how a hospital or outpatient surgery works. The hospital is not trying to have any liable suits, and even if you choose no treatment you still have to sign some hospital liability form that you refused treatment and leave the hospital. How about this go; find a real hospital get the treatment you need sign the discharge papers and keep it moving or are you in a mental state of mind. JUST A THOUGHT!!!!

CALLER QUESTION:
Okay, should I get a doctor's note?

RESPONSE:
I would suggest you do, and more than that, stop telling that story about not receiving discharge papers from the hospital after you had prostate surgery.

CALLER QUESTION:
Yeah, 'cause my real concern is them taking down my pants in front of everyone, or will they take me into a room?

RESPONSE:
Most likely if it comes to that, then yes, they will take you behind a screen and privately check you. And having your doctor's note as to why the bag is strapped to your leg will perhaps speed up your time for making your flight. A word to the wise: when you have any kind of surgery again, wait for the doctor's discharge papers and sign them; your bill will be in the mail! JUST A THOUGHT!!!

CALLER QUESTION:
I want to know if there is a shuttle to Pennsylvania?

RESPONSE:
Yes, here is the name of the company, the number and schedules, and prices, but call them to make your reservations!

CALLER QUESTION:
Is that the shuttle to Pennsylvania?

RESPONSE:
No, it's the shuttle to the moon (fly me to the moon and let me gaze upon the stars), FRANK SINATRA; stay focused, I know that short-term memory can be a MOTHER! JUST A THOUGHT!!!

CALLER QUESTION:
I want someone paged at Delta International terminal.

RESPONSE:
Call this number for a Delta page.

CALLER QUESTION:
What's this number for? They told me to call Delta International to page the person and the number I have!

RESPONSE:
That's the number for the terminal, which has international flights coming in.

Dorinda Henderson

CALLER QUESTION:
They told me to call the terminal to have them paged!

RESPONSE:
This is definitely too much back and forth! XYZ is an international airport, and if you're looking to page at this airport you have to call the airline in that terminal.

This shouldn't be "I have the solution, now find the problem"; the solution to your dilemma is that Delta doesn't have a terminal paging for its international flight. You call Delta and tell them you want to page a passenger on their international flight, because by the time you get this the person you wanted paged will be paging you at home! JUST A THOUGHT!!!

Day Twenty-One:

CALLER QUESTION:
I want to know, when the airline gives a time for a flight and they say estimated, what does that mean?

RESPONSE:
It means the time of the flight has been calculated from where the flight is coming from to the arrival time of its landing at the airport.

CALLER QUESTION:
So, if a flight is to come at 9:02 p.m. that means it can come at 9:30 p.m., right?

RESPONSE:
No, that's not what I said; what time are you expecting the flight to land?

CALLER QUESTION:
At 9:30 p.m.

RESPONSE:
Then that's when the plane will arrive! You're putting too much time into estimated time and actual time. What time, the right time, the real time, time and time, time is late, time is early. And

apparently you have too much on your hands and I don't want you wasting any more of mine; relax and enjoy your time. JUST A THOUGHT!!!

CALLER QUESTION:
I'm calling to find out if a cargo company would help load cargo on my truck.

RESPONSE:
What cargo company are you interested in; do you have a name for the company?

CALLER QUESTION:
Oh, I don't have one yet, but I want to send some fish!

RESPONSE:
First find out the cargo company name you want to use for cargo; second, call them to find out if they'll help you load your cargo to your truck or vehicle; and third, what's the point of this call? You have no clue as to what cargo company you want to use; is it the airline or private cargo company? Why call here to find out if the cargo company you don't have may help you load your fish to your truck or vehicle? Let's say you called and were given a name to a cargo company and didn't give the contents of the item; you would have gotten a number to that company and they would assist your needs. That's like you wouldn't call Macy's to ask what Gimbels is doing. Have a vision, a goal, and a mission and get some strategy in your life; it can go a long way! JUST A THOUGHT!!!

CALLER QUESTION:
I'm looking for a flight coming from Egypt!

RESPONSE:
Call EgyptAir; the number is…

CALLER QUESTION:
I tried the number for EgyptAir and I got a rapid busy.

RESPONSE:
Where in Egypt is the flight coming from?

CALLER QUESTION:
I don't know! Oh, I think it's Cairo.

RESPONSE:
Hold on, please. (Looking for flight on information on the computer; found flight and gave caller the time and terminal for flight.) You know, you can catch more flies with honey than, you can catch them with blank. And you can keep the threats about "give me your supervisor or your boss" do nothing for me or your situation, or "you work for me and I pay your salary, you do what you're supposed to do, do as I say"; this to me is all slave mentality and just cruel and nasty to another person. You called this company for assistance with some information you didn't have ; that's why you called. And I don't believe in the customer is always right, especially this one. And the way you've conducted yourself over this phone conversation , you should

feel privileged that the person you're talking isn't a machine and is still trying to help you with all the rhetoric you have given them. I suggest you practice how to be a little humbler, like hot an apple pie and a warm glass of milk. JUST A THOUGHT!!!

I know you may be tired of reading these parking-information fragments throughout the book, but trust me, each story shares its own merits in many different ways. Let me go on record saying most of these people are calling from the Tri-State area inquiring about parking at the airports. Yes, it's true, some prices do vary depending on which airport you are parked at ; just like all the signage for the terminals at the airports are different! PAY ATTENTION PEOPLE

CALLER QUESTION:
Short question; good morning, I'd like to know how much short-term parking is?

RESPONSE:
Short term is $15.00 per day.

CALLER QUESTION:
Here's the long-term parking question; is that 24 hours per day?

RESPONSE:
Here's the long and short answer: 24 hours is a day, so yes, it's per day, which means in New York the time goes counter-clockwise and starting from 12 all the way around again will be 24 hours, and some places around the world that time comes twice a day! JUST A THOUGHT!!!

CALLER QUESTION:
I'm calling for a number to an airline.

RESPONSE:
Okay, what airline?

CALLER QUESTION:
They went out of business!

RESPONSE:
Oh, then there is no way I can obtain the number if they went out of business!

CALLER QUESTION:
So, I have to call the airline?

RESPONSE:
Let's go over this call for a minute: you called asking about an airline that has gone out of business and this you are certain of, right? And don't let me rely on just your information; I have methods of my own to find out what I need to know at the airport. And I concur that airline is out of business, so I tell you I can't help you obtain that information. Then you come back and say should I call the airline? Hmm, no, what you should do is call me back when you get someone from that airline and they give the information you need! JUST A THOUGHT!!!

TODAY IS A WINDY AND RAINY DAY, SO PREPARE FOR THE PEOPLE'S ATTITUDES AND ABNORMAL QUESTIONING!

CALLER QUESTION:
I'm calling to find out, when can I make my reservation to travel?

RESPONSE:
You can call any time before your flight; it can't be an hour before you want to travel. You may perhaps be able to get a flight the same day but at a later time!

CALLER QUESTION:
SMART ASS

RESPONSE:
I know I am but what are you? You sound like you are grown enough to know when it's time to make your reservation, so why are you calling information to get confirmation on something you apparently don't know anything about! It doesn't take a brain surgeon to know if they want to make a reservation for the theater, for dinner, for a car rental, or in your case an airline, and all that was mentioned was that you need to do it in advance. The only permission I need was in elementary school when there was a field trip and I needed my parent to sign the permission slip to go! But again, this is coming from a SMART ASS! JUST A THOUGHT!!!

CALLER QUESTION:
My aunt had a flu shot two days ago, but she got sick and she has a flight tomorrow. I want to know, will they let her fly?

RESPONSE:
Okay, why wouldn't she be able to fly?

CALLER QUESTION:
That's why I'm calling, to see if they will let her fly!

RESPONSE:
Who's going to stop her?

CALLER QUESTION:
I don't know!

RESPONSE:
If she isn't feeling good enough to fly, then she should make other arrangements with the airline in advance, not the day of… look, no one knows she had a flu shot and got sick but her and you. Now, if she was leaving the country and she had a contagious virus that could go airborne when she coughed or sneezed, then yes, there would be a need for concern. Bottom line: if your aunt doesn't feel well enough to travel that day, then she should consult her doctor and tell him/her how she feels after the flu shot. A person, I feel, should know their body and how it feels before and after any shot or medication, 'cause there are no shots for medication, just common sense, and have some to get through your day! JUST A THOUGHT!!!

CALLER QUESTION:
My husband called and said his flight has been canceled!

RESPONSE:
Okay, why was his flight canceled, did he say?

CALLER QUESTION:
He doesn't know!

RESPONSE:
Your husband called you and told you this?

CALLER QUESTION:
Yes, and when I call the airline there is no answer!

RESPONSE:
Here's the airline number I have here at the airport; try it!

CALLER QUESTION:
I tried that number and still no answer!

RESPONSE:
Is your husband in that terminal right now, do you know? Do you know if your husband is near any airline personnel, so he can ask what's going on?

CALLER QUESTION:
Give me your supervisor!

RESPONSE:
I'm more than glad to connect you to my supervisor. I no longer want to talk to you or your husband at this point; you both are

Tweedledum and Tweedledee! He's in the terminal and his flight has been canceled and he has you call information, not even in the same airport or state or possibly country, to find out why his flight was canceled, and I have to figure this out—please. You don't need a supervisor to talk to you or your husband! You two are like two ships in the night passing each other! JUST A THOUGHT!!!

CALLER QUESTION:
I'm calling about my mother's walker; we came to pick her up from the airport and we forgot her walker!

RESPONSE:
You have to call lost and found for that airline.

CALLER QUESTION:
Okay, because we are two hours away and she needs her walker!

RESPONSE:
How did you forget your mother's walker that she obvious needs to walk with! How did you not notice that—maybe when she went to stand from the wheelchair, or when you were carrying her, and she started to get heavy, or when you saw her crawling to the baggage area for her luggage! It had to be brought to your attention way before you left the luggage area and got two hours away! I wonder what will happen when someone forgets your walker one day! JUST A THOUGHT!!!

CALLER QUESTION:

I want to know, is there a plane...umm, umm...or a bus, no, I don't mean a bus!

RESPONSE:

Slow down—do you want a train? And where are you going?

CALLER QUESTION:

Yeah, the train...does the train go from XYZ to EFG airport?

RESPONSE:

No, there isn't a train that does that!

CALLER QUESTION:

So how would I get from the airport to EFG?

RESPONSE:

Take what is called the A train to 34th street in Manhattan.

CALLER QUESTION:

Then what?

RESPONSE:

Then just like you called this number for information, you find someone at the train station and ask them where you get the path train to EFG airport!

CALLER QUESTION:

I'm just asking you, miss, 'cause I don't know, and you don't have to sound like that!

RESPONSE:
I just answered your question in its entirety, and now you want to analyze how my voice sounds! Have you listened to how you sound! JUST A THOUGHT!!!

CALLER QUESTION:
How much would it cost to come from Guyana?

RESPONSE:
I have no idea; you'd have to call the airline that goes to and from Guyana! Do you have an airline? If so, I can give you a number!

CALLER QUESTION:
Oh, no, I don't!

RESPONSE:
Where in Guyana are you going, is it Georgetown?

CALLER QUESTION:
I don't know, but how much does it cost coming from Guyana?

RESPONSE:
First of all, can you afford it—apparently not; secondly, you or whoever is traveling to or from Guyana should call a travel agent and get this information, because I'm not a travel agent and don't have the answer you need! JUST A THOUGHT!!!

Day Twenty-Two

CALLER QUESTION:
I want to know if I can check a laundry bag?

RESPONSE:
Do you mean a duffel bag like the military have?

CALLER QUESTION:
No, it's a laundry bag with a string that you pull to close it!

RESPONSE:
What airline are you traveling with?

CALLER QUESTION:
American Airline.

RESPONSE:
Call this number. But my suggestion is that you should buy some kind of luggage a bit stronger than a duffel bag, the reason being that I've gotten several complaints about people having big suitcases damaged or broken into and property missing or stolen. What I'm saying is, your laundry bag has no chance in hell of one of the above not happening to it. Another suggestion is, keep your laundry bag in the laundry room; this isn't a laundromat! JUST A THOUGHT!!!

CALLER QUESTION:
What time do the stores open in the terminals?

RESPONSE:
What kind of store?

CALLER QUESTION:
A liquor store!

RESPONSE:
It's called a duty-free shop, and they are open a little later in the terminals. The only way you can purchase from them is if you're traveling overseas and you have a ticket to prove that. If you're traveling within the United States, my suggestion is to go to your local liquor store and buy your liquor the day before   getting some towels, and wrap the bottle or bottles up very securely, then place them between your clothes in your luggage. If you want to carry-on, that's not going to happening so go to Walgreen's, CVS, or wherever you can buy a big mouthwash bottle, pour it out and fill it up with your liquor, then go into the restroom and drink your nerve away! JUST A THOUGHT!!!

CALLER QUESTION:
My girlfriend wants to come and stay a month with me in New York, and she wants to bring her three-year-old daughter. But

she said they told her at the airport she had to buy a round-trip ticket for her daughter as well!

RESPONSE:
Why does she have to buy a round-trip ticket—she's coming from New York, right? Where is she trying to go?

CALLER QUESTION:
No, she's coming from Puerto Rico.

RESPONSE:
Okay, you do know that Puerto Rico is a commonwealth state of the United States, which is considered property of the United States, so there is no need for a passport or buying a round-trip ticket!

CALLER QUESTION:
She told them. She's in court with the father and the courts awarded them joint custody of the daughter. And the father gave her the mother a written permission letter allowing her to take her daughter to New York.

RESPONSE:
First of all, the story sounds fishy. You said she was going to court for child custody; either she won the case and was awarded full custody and she wouldn't need a written permission from the father, or they have half custody, which means that maybe half of the year one parent gets the child and then the other half the other parent gets the child. Now, if she never went to court and they are in the process then the child can go with any parent anywhere. And if the judge awarded one of them full custody,

then there are visitation rights and yes, a round-trip ticket has to be purchased. But the fishy part is, it sounds like the mother wants to stay in New York more than the month you mentioned, I'm just saying, and doesn't want the daughter to be with the father, Hummmm? JUST A THOUGHT!!!

CALLER QUESTION:
I noticed that my passport expired five months ago, and I called the airline and they said I can travel. And I want to know what the airport has to say!

RESPONSE:
Five months your passport expired—are you traveling international or domestic? So, make this call short and sweet: the airport has nothing to do with your passport. Another clue with your passport: the expired time is 10 years for renewal, so the clue to you is, when was the last time you used your passport and didn't realize that the time is going to come that I have to renew my passport? Now laws have changed, and you have to renew your passport six months before traveling, and I know this is another grownup responsibility that is placed upon us, but we have to be responsible someday as grownups for something instead of blaming it on the rain! JUST A THOUGHT!!!

CALLED QUESTION:
I want to know, if I bought my ticket today and I'm traveling November 11, 2009, can I pick up my ticket before that date?

RESPONSE:
Let's start like this: did you call the airline and pay for your ticket or did you do it online?

CALLER QUESTION:
Yes, I did!

RESPONSE:
Yes, you did it online or by phone? And with either, did you receive a confirmation number? That gives you proof of purchase for your ticket.

CALLER QUESTION:
I got a confirmation number, but I can't remember when I called the airline, so I came to the airport and they told me my ticket was voided out!

RESPONSE:
There is a lot going on with this call! What's the name of the airline you made your reservation with?

CALLER QUESTION:
Delta.

RESPONSE:
Here's another number; try it, and the only thing I can leave you with is, you should have called before coming to the airport. You should have paid your credit card bill or at least checked before using it. And besides, if you don't have enough on your credit card, it wouldn't have gone that far without the airline telling you it was voided out. Oh, maybe you missed that flight and the

airline voided that ticket, you think? Remember, you said you didn't remember when you called the airline! However, check your balance before doing any more transactions on it, 'cause you may forget you have a credit card! JUST A THOUGHT!!!

CALLER QUESTION:
Some people are coming into ABC airport at 7:30 p.m. today.

RESPONSE:
Where from? What airline?

CALLER QUESTION:
Oh, I don't know! All they said was that they were coming and landing at 7:30 p.m. Oh, wait a minute, I found out where; it's St. Louis.

RESPONSE:
Let me check my information; hold on, please. I don't see any flight from St. Louis at 7:30 p.m. coming to ABC airport today!

CALLER QUESTION:
Maybe it's South Dakota!

RESPONSE:
Okay, maybe it is Mars, but I don't have time to guesstimate when these people are coming into this airport at that time, and my day isn't long enough to go through this with you on this journey. Some advice: when that actual time and day comes, wait for them to land and call you to let you know they landed and the time

they did. And I strongly suggest you write it down and have them repeat it, then tell it to another friend that was there with you to repeat it, so now you'll have four ears, which are better than your two. In your case, the more the better! JUST A THOUGHT!!!

CALLER QUESTION: With daylight saving time, does the airport change its time?

RESPONSE:
Yes, the airline automatically changes their time to adjust to their flight schedules!

CALLER QUESTION:
Just checking; just wanted to know, so it's one hour earlier, like the rest of the world?

RESPONSE:
Let's break this down for you briefly. The world's time is different from state to state, except Arizona they don't mess with God! But for the rest of us, we do. Therefore, when spring turns to summer the time springs ahead, and when fall turns to winter the time falls back, and each way is 1 hourone-hour difference in time. This only applies for Eastern Time; Pacific, Mountain, and Central are different, but let's not confuse you any more than you are. So, we are staying Eastern for now; the season is summer, so your time is an extra hour and it stays lighter, so instead of 1 p.m. it's 2 p.m. This isn't hard to understand, like you'll know when you fall and hit your head it's time to lie back down, and let you get the right time to spring ahead! JUST A THOUGHT!!!

CALLER QUESTION:
How much does it cost, because I want to visit my relatives in Italy?

RESPONSE:
I'm not a travel agent, nor do I have airline prices!

CALLER QUESTION:
Okay, can you send me a package to my house?

RESPONSE:
WHAT!!

CALLER QUESTION:
Can you send a package to my house?

RESPONSE:
No, I can't send anything to your house, miss!

CALLER QUESTION:
So, do you have prices and times?

RESPONSE:
NO, NO, NO! What part did you miss in this conversation—the listening when I said I wasn't a travel agent or an airline to give you prices or the hearing yourself talk? Let's flip a coin: heads you weren't listening or tails you didn't adjust your hearing aid. I'll take listening for 500, Alex. JUST A THOUGHT!!!
MESSAGE: here is the concept of listening and hearing!

LISTENING = ABLE TO RETURN CONVERSATION WITH THE OTHER PERSON, WHICH MEANS BY WAY OF QUESTIONING OR ELABORATING ON THE CONVERSATION WITH SAID PERSON AND/OR PARTICIPATION IN SAID CONVERSATION AS WELL AS EXCHANGING IDEAS, THOUGHTS, AND OPINIONS. HEARING = HERE IS THE CONCEPT OF HEARING, WHICH MEAN SOUNDS, i.e., HORNS, TRAINS, BUSES, GUNSHOTS, TELEPHONES, SNORING, PLANES, LAUGHTER, MUSIC, CRYING, YELLING, AND THEN THERE ARE WORDS THAT PEOPLE FORMULATE, WHICH TRANSLATES TO LISTENING.

CALLER QUESTION:
Do you have airline information?

RESPONSE:
It depends on what information you need!

CALLER QUESTION:
Oh, you don't have airline information?

RESPONSE:
Can you give me a hint? When I answered the call I said Airport Information; now did that sound like Boardwalk Casino? I don't think so! I have airline locations in the terminals, I have airline numbers, I have airline lost and found numbers, I have ticket-counter numbers for the airlines, I have baggage and storage numbers for the airlines, pretty much any number you need for

any particular airline at more than one airport. Here's another one that bites the dust; YOU'RE NOT LISTENING! JUST A THOUGHT!!!

CALLER QUESTION:
Can I travel with an old passport?

RESPONSE:
How old is the passport?

CALLER QUESTION:
2005!

RESPONSE:
Can't use it!

CALLER QUESTION:
WHAT!

RESPONSE:
I repeat, can't use it! If it was a month before it was expired you may have had a chance, but the laws have changed, and they want you to renew passports six months prior to traveling. Perhaps you may be able to get an emergency passport in Manhattan, but it's going to cost you!

CALLER QUESTION:
I'm leaving at 5 a.m.!

RESPONSE:

Not this 5 a.m., with a passport that expired a year ago! Imagine, if everyone traveled or was allowed to travel with an expired passport, why would anyone need one?

CALLER QUESTION:

Can I use a library card or something with my picture on it?

RESPONSE:

I got one even better: how about the picture that used to come in the wallets when you bought one! Are you serious right now? I know when you first got your passport that it had to renew every 10 years—oh, you apparently didn't get that memo; well, you've just been served! JUST A THOUGHT!!!

CALLER QUESTION:

I'm calling in to check on a flight that is now 12 hours delayed!

RESPONSE:

How do you know it's 12 hours delayed?

CALLER QUESTION:

I checked with the airline website! So, can you check your information?

RESPONSE:

Hold on, please (back)… The flight is estimated at 1:20 a.m. in terminal 13.

CALLER QUESTION:
Are you sure that's the right terminal?

RESPONSE:
No, I just made that up. I like giving people wrong information, so they can call back and I have to repeat myself. Better still, you said you were on the airline website, good that makes you smarter than the average bear and got your information. Now the next step is finding out the correct terminal on that site or, better still, call the airline directly and ask them for the correct terminal number, 'cause you're doubting my information and I don't want that to happen. 'Cause you have the world in your hands with the Web! JUST A THOUGHT!!!

CALLER QUESTION:
I'm looking for an ASU union number at the airport!

RESPONSE:
I never heard of an ASU union at the airport!

CALLER QUESTION:
My husband used to work at the airport and this was his union name!

RESPONSE:
What's the name of the company he worked for at the airport?

CALLER QUESTION:
Hold on. She asks someone in the background, comes back to the phone, and says, Control!

RESPONSE:
Control what?

CALLER QUESTION:
Oh, I don't know, Control what!

RESPONSE:
What do you mean you don't know, if this is your husband and his job we're talking about?

CALLER QUESTION:
My husband died!

RESPONSE:
If this was your husband, then you should have had all of his papers in order and called the union that he was with and gotten all the necessary information you need. Now, on the other hand, if you were common-law and weren't legally married, then you needed to have had that conversation with him before he died, and if you are an ex-wife trying to find out if he had some union financial business you feel you're entitled to, I think you've been voted off the island, hmm! JUST A THOUGHT!!!

CALLER QUESTION:
I'm traveling with this airline and they lost my baggage!

RESPONSE: CO-WORKER:
Co-worker: did you call the particular airline baggage?

CALLER QUESTION:
They told me to call you!

RESPONSE: CO-WORKER:
Co-worker: No, you have to call the airline baggage; here's the number: ---,---,----.

CALLER QUESTION:
Who I'm I talking to now?

RESPONSE: CO-WORKER:
Co-worker: This is the number for the airline (conversation ends!).

CALLER QUESTION:
I just spoke to a person who was very rude, and she didn't let me finish my question!

RESPONSE:
Now I get the call. How may I help you?
CALL QUESTION:
I just called and that person I spoke with was rude and not polite, and she didn't let me ask my question, which was, should I call the baggage number she gave me?

RESPONSE:
Is the number I'm giving you the same number she gave you?

CALLER QUESTION:
Yeah, that's the same number, but I wanted to know!

RESPONSE:
Okay, now that you know it's the same number, what was the sense in wasting your time playing match-up numbers instead of going ahead and calling the number for your information? And you really must think you are special, getting two people to answer your question twice; be careful, the third one might be a charm! JUST A THOUGHT!!!

CALLER QUESTION:
I'm traveling to China and I want to know the weight of the luggage allowed?

RESPONSE:
Two suitcases, 50 pounds per suitcase is allowed; anything more, you'd pay extra!

CALLER QUESTION:
Okay, I just called to ask about the suitcases, and you said 50 pounds per suitcase!

RESPONSE:
Yes.

CALLER QUESTION:
I want to bring only one suitcase!

RESPONSE:
Okay, if you're allowed two at 50 pounds and you're only bringing one, what's your question?

CALLER QUESTION:
You don't have to sound nasty about it!

RESPONSE:
Oh, I'm not being nasty; it's called being logical and trying to figure out when you're going to do the math, or were you absent for that class that day? If you have two of something and you take away one, how many do you have? Elementary, Watson, elementary! JUST A THOUGHT!!!

CALLER QUESTION:
I have a question: my son missed his flight because he helped break up an altercation with another passenger, so I'm wondering if the airline will accommodate my son on another flight? When I talked with the airline they said he would have to pay for another ticket, which would be $400.00! Who can I speak to about this situation?

RESPONSE:
Technically, your son should have made his flight and left that flight alone! JUST A THOUGHT!!!

CALLER QUESTION:
I want to know about taking pills on the plane! Do they have to be labeled on the container with my name on it?

RESPONSE:
You're allowed to take pills onboard with you that don't have to be in prescribed pill bottles, as long as it isn't liquid; then it has to be three ounces.

CALLER QUESTION:
Okay, as long as it isn't liquids, right?

RESPONSE:
Right!

CALLER QUESTION:
What is your name?

RESPONSE:
Why do you want my name?

CALLER QUESTION:
In case I talk to someone I can tell them I spoke with you!

RESPONSE:
Hold on, please (dialing the number that can assist her with this question). I listened on the phone to the conversation and the person confirmed the same thing I told her in the beginning of this call!

CALLER QUESTION:
So, I don't need to put pills in a container?

RESPONSE:
What didn't you understand from two people saying the same thing? Yes, you can bring the pills on the plane without a con-

tainer, and yes, you can bring the pills on the plane. How about this: why don't you take those pills in your mouth, swallow, and now all of your problems are solved! JUST A THOUGHT!!!

Day Twenty-Three:

That was my final call. Whatever my readers take away from this book, if anything, I'd like it to be this: when you're traveling, whether it's to or from your origin or destination, via airplane, boat, train, vehicle, bike, skates, or walking, most of the time, it should be a pleasant experience, safe and possibly fun, but mainly smart! Think before you speak, plan or map out your adventure or travels, do some research, write down any question you may feel important at the time. Have a clear mind so your thoughts can be followed and make sense when calling for information so the other person on the receiving end can expedite your call quickly and clearly. It's okay if you don't have all the answers; hell, neither do I! I'm not the smart nail in the wall, but I do know how to ask for what I want when I want it and be very clear about it as well. However, when you stand to be corrected, don't flare up with this hilarious attitude. It's a process that is called learning; this is business known for its business of given proper information to travelers trying to find their way through this thing called flying! Information isn't there to cure your illness, pay bills, put food on your table, send your children to college, make funeral arrangements, marriage, divorce, child support, or other life experiences people have and are going through. Although I did have those experiences with a lot of those calls—I almost went for my psychologist's degree! What I'm saying is, just follow some basic rules when traveling and you should be fine and enjoy what could your first time dealing with the airports and airlines, even with security the way it is—better safe than sorry; just relax! I've had a blast writing this book and I hope you had one reading it with the most outlandish, hilarious, ridiculous calls coming from the most confused, scary, excitable, misinformed, impatient, uneducated, nasty, sweet, kind, and friendly people on the other end of the phone. It has been truly and sincerely an amazing thirty days! Wait a minute, what am I saying—it's been a truly amazing thirty years! HAPPY TRAVELING—remember, watch your trip, you might have a long fall! JUST A THOUGHT!!! PEACE...